D1310026

PRACTICE MAKES PERFECT

Preparation for
State Reading
Assessments

LEVEL
10

PRESTWICK HOUSE
INCORPORATED

P.O. Box 658 • Clayton, Delaware 19938

Author: Sondra Y. Abel

Editor: Mary C. Beardsley

Reviewing Teachers: Barbara Bretherick, Wellington FL
Catherine O. Routh, Helena, GA

Cover Design: Larry Knox

Production: Jerry Clark

Prestwick House, Inc.
P.O. Box 658 • Clayton, Delaware 19938
Tel: 1.800.932.4593
Fax: 1.888.718.9333
Web: www.prestwickhouse.com

ISBN-10   1-58049-319-X
ISBN-13   978-1-58049-319-2

Preparation for
State Reading
Assessments

Table of Contents

Introduction to the Student — LEVEL 10

How to Take a Reading Comprehension Test

Taking a reading comprehension test does not have to be a stressful event. The following tips and methods can be used to make your test-taking efforts more effective and your results more accurate.

FOCUS:

When you read a comprehension passage, you should try to identify the following:

- main idea - author's attitude or tone - author's purpose.

Many comprehension questions focus on your ability to determine what the author is trying to say and why he or she is saying it. Think about whether the author is biased: does he or she support, criticize, or remain objective about the subject? What clues show the writer's attitude?

While you read, you should imagine yourself as the test writer.

- Which pieces of information do you think are important?
- Is the passage about a person or a group of people?
- What is that person's or group's message to the world?
- What questions would you write about the passage?

When you come across a point that stands out, make a mental note of it. Ask yourself why the author included it. Information that seems to have a special purpose often shows up in the questions.

TIPS:

In order to determine an author's attitude toward the subject, look for emotionally charged words, such as *tragically, sadly, unfortunately, surprisingly, amazingly, justly,* etc. These words indicate an author's bias—whether the author sides with or against the subject of the passage. Simple words tell you a lot about the author's feelings.

Frequently, you are asked to identify the main idea of a passage. These types of questions do not always use the words *main idea*. They may ask for the most appropriate title or the statement with which the author would most likely agree or disagree. Pick the answer that is true for the entire passage. If no choice relates to the entire selection, choose the answer that is supported by most of the passage.

You will also encounter questions that ask you to define a word or find the most appropriate synonym. These questions check your ability to use context clues, not your vocabulary knowledge. Sometimes, you will find more than one seemingly correct answer, but when you look at the word as it is used in the paragraph, you can choose the best synonym for the situation.

Some questions are open-ended and require you to write an answer. You must write two-to-four complete sentences to answer these types of questions. The person who scores your answer will look for you to explain yourself, so be sure to support your opinion with details from the passage.

Finally, when it comes to taking timed tests, many people feel pressured to race through the work so that they complete all of it. Remember, though, that careful reading cannot be rushed. So, what can you do? When you cannot decide the answer to a question, skip it and come back to it after you have answered the rest of the questions for that passage. You may even find the answer when you are working on other questions. If you still cannot answer it, make your best guess and move on, rather than spend too much time trying to figure out one question, leaving yourself insufficient time to answer the rest accurately.

Some people suggest reading the questions before you read the passage so that you know what information you need. If this works for you, that is terrific! For many people, however, this uses valuable time and results in too much information to remember. This breaks their concentration, and they cannot focus on what they read. If you cannot focus on both the questions and the reading at one time, read the passage first, concentrating on what you read. If you need to look back at the passage to answer the questions, go ahead and do so. The point to be made here is that you should work in a manner that is comfortable for you. When you find a technique that works for you, use it!

REMEMBER THESE THREE EXTREMELY IMPORTANT POINTS:

1. **Read the directions and questions carefully!**
   Look for tricky words, such as *not, always, true, opposite,* etc. These words greatly affect the answer to the question.

2. **If you cannot remember what you just read, read it again, and pay attention to it!**

3. **Always read all the answer choices!**

You may choose the wrong answer and miss the correct one entirely if you stop reading once you think you have found the answer. There may be a better choice farther down the list, and you will miss it if you do not read it.

Model Passage

The following model passage demonstrates effective use of the reading tips and strategies. You will see that there are underlined words and phrases in the passage and notes in the margins. The notes in the margins refer to the underlined portions of the passage and serve as examples of the way you should think about the passage. These notes include questions you should ask yourself or comments you should make to yourself as you read.

The Railroads Connect

[1]This passage will be about the disorder of the "Wedding of the Rails" celebration.

On May 10, 1869, the Transcontinental Railroad was finally connected after years of hard work and confusion, but the celebration of the "Wedding of the Rails" was plagued by disorder and misunderstanding.[1]

[2]What are the funny errors?

[3]The points are organized. The word *first* tells me to look for *second*, etc. Look for *next* and *finally*.

[4]Wow, that is only four days before the ceremony.

[5]Wow, $400 of his own gold! Why? What kind of question will the test ask about this?

[6]I should look at the context of these boldfaced words. What do they mean?

[7]Those spikes were just dropped in the holes!

[8]This was a huge event if the telegraph was going to relay the sound.

Of course, the real story is a comedy of errors.[2] First[3] the actual location of the event was Promontory Summit, Utah, but since this was not on the map, the press reported that it occurred at Promontory Point; therefore, postcards, souvenirs, and even textbooks to this day bear the name of the incorrect location. Second, on May 4, 1869,[4] the president of the Central Pacific Railroad, Leland Stanford, revealed to his friend, David Hewes, that no commemorative item had been made for the event. Upset by this fact, Hewes attempted to have a solid gold rail made, but after failing to find someone to finance it, he had $400 worth of his own gold melted and cast[5] as the "Golden Spike," which was then engraved[6] for the occasion. Three other spikes were also made for the event. The next problem arose when the event had to be postponed because disgruntled[6] workers and poor weather conditions delayed the arrival of officials from the Union Pacific Railroad. Finally, on May 10, 1869, the officials from both the Union Pacific and the Central Pacific railroads convened for the celebration. A special laurelwood railroad tie was laid in place at the junction, and the specially-made spikes were dropped into pre-drilled holes. Not one of them was actually hammered into place.[7] Then, the laurelwood tie and spikes were replaced with a standard tie and regular iron spikes. The last spike and the hammer were connected to the telegraph line so that the entire nation could hear[8] the "Wedding of the

[9] The name of the event is mentioned again. This must be important.

Rails."[9] The sound of the hammer hitting the spike would then travel across the country through the telegraph line. Leland Stanford was given the first swing, but he missed[10] the spike and hit the wooden tie. Thomas Durant, vice president of the Union Pacific Railroad, swung at the spike, but missed entirely. In the end, a railroad employee hammered in the final tie,[10] and the telegraph operator sent the message to the country: "D-O-N-E."

[10] That is funny—after all of the problems, the important people who were supposed to hammer the spike could not do it.

[11] That is funny, too. I cannot believe no one showed up. It seems as if no one cared.

Not so surprisingly, when the fiftieth anniversary celebration was scheduled, not one person showed up.[11] Maybe they all went to Promontory Point.

---

1. **Which of the following best states the author's purpose?**
    - **A.** to make fun of the Transcontinental Railroad
    - **B.** to make an accurate portrayal of an important event in railroad history
    - **C.** to explain the importance of the Golden Spike
    - **D.** to describe how history books sometimes contain incorrect information

(B) *The author accurately describes the confusion and mishaps surrounding the "Wedding of the Rails" celebration. All other answer choices are merely supporting points in the passage.*

---

2. **Which of the following would be the best title for this passage?**
    - **A.** The Golden Spike Disaster
    - **B.** Where the Railroads Meet
    - **C.** Leland Stanford's Spike
    - **D.** The Wedding of the Rails

(D) *The passage is about the entire "Wedding of the Rails" ceremony. After all, the ceremony's title is mentioned twice in the passage, making it significant information appropriate for the title. Although the event was riddled with errors, it would not be considered a disaster. Finally, the passage does not focus solely on Leland Stanford's spike or where the event occurred.*

3. **Which of the following did not lend to the confusion on May 10, 1869?**
   A. the telegraph operator
   B. poor weather conditions
   C. last-minute planning
   D. uncertainty about the location

(A) *The telegraph operator does not make any errors. The poor weather postponed officials; last minute planning required a friend to donate his own gold for the commemorative spike; uncertainty about the location led to incorrect information.*

4. **As used in the passage, the word *engraved* most nearly means**
   A. molded.
   B. decorated.
   C. transported.
   D. purchased.

(B) *If the spike was <u>engraved</u> for the occasion, it must have been decorated to show its commemorative purpose. <u>Molded</u> is not the answer because the passage already stated that the gold was melted and cast. Although the spike would have to be <u>transported</u>, the context is discussing the making of the spike, not the shipping of the spike. Finally, the gold was already <u>purchased</u> since it belonged to Hewes.*

5. **Based on the information provided in the passage, what can you infer is the reason for David Hewes' melting his own gold to make the spike?**
   A. He was angry that no one would help him.
   B. He wanted to become famous for his contribution to the Transcontinental Railroad.
   C. He could find no one willing to pay for or donate the gold.
   D. He had more gold than he needed, so he was willing to give some away.

(C) *Hewes tried to find someone to finance a rail but was unsuccessful. Had he found someone willing to pay or donate at least something, then he would not have had to use his own resources. Since he looked for someone to finance a golden rail instead of financing it himself, we can infer that he did not have an overabundance of gold. There are no clues to imply he was searching for fame. Finally, the passage states that he was upset that there was item made to commemorate the event, but no mention of his being angry at finding no one willing to help.*

6. *Answer the following question using complete sentences:*

   Why does the author call the "Wedding of the Rails" a "comedy of errors"?

The event is humorous because it was a major celebration of the uniting of the country's rails, which was a massive undertaking, and everything that could go wrong did. Railroad officials arrived late because their workers were unhappy, the commemorative spike was not even hammered in, and a railroad employee, not any of the officials who organized the celebration, completed the actual connection of the rails. As a final taunt, no one showed up for the fiftieth anniversary celebration.

DIRECTIONS: *Read the passage and answer the questions that follow it.*

Salvador Dalí

SALVADOR DALÍ WAS BORN on May 11, 1904, in Catalonia, Spain, into a comfortable middle-class family. His father, a lawyer, was a strict disciplinarian. Dalí had a sister three years his junior named Ana Mariá and an older brother (also named Salvador) who died before Dalí's birth. Salvador received formal art training while attending Municipal Drawing School. Dalí's first art exhibit, which featured charcoal drawings, was held in the family's home in 1917. Two years later, his work was placed on exhibit at the Municipal Theatre in Figueres. Dalí's mother, who nurtured his talent and encouraged his drawing, died of cancer in 1921, when Dalí was sixteen. When Dalí's father then married his deceased wife's sister, Dalí resented the marriage.

The following year, Dalí moved to the students' residence in Madrid where he met filmmaker Luis Buñuel and poet Federico Garcia Lorca. He drew attention to himself by wearing long hair, sideburns, and a twisted mustache while outfitting himself in vintage clothing from former centuries. He experimented with the art of Cubism, which reduces natural objects to geometric shapes, and Dada, an illogical and discordant art form. During his first visit to Paris in 1926, he met with Pablo Picasso. Dalí developed his own style after studying with Picasso and other artists and examined popular artistic trends of the time. His complex works often incited debates among critics and attracted wide attention.

Dalí did not limit his works to just the canvas. In 1929, he collaborated with Buñuel on a surrealist short film titled *Un chien andalou*. It was at this time that he met his future wife, Gala, a Russian immigrant, who was eleven years older than he. He soon joined a surrealist group in Paris and held many exhibits of his work. Surrealists interpreted Dalí's work, which often featured dream visions and odd objects, as creative examinations of the **subconscious**. Although Dalí's work has transformed in response to his own stages of life, religious awakenings, and governmental changes, Dalí's work and **eccentricity** will continue to receive public attention for years to come. **O**

QUESTIONS

1. Why did the author write this passage?
- **A.** to inform the reader about Cubism
- **B.** to explain how Dalí became famous
- **C.** to describe the art form inspired by Dada
- **D.** to inform the reader of the sources of Dalí's inspiration

2. Which of the following would be the best title for this passage?
- **A.** Dalí and Dada
- **B.** Salvador and Surrealism
- **C.** Art in Spain
- **D.** Dalí's Influence

3. Which of the following best describes the reason for the first paragraph?
- **A.** It explains what first interested Dalí in art.
- **B.** It informs the reader about Dalí's relationship with his father.
- **C.** It describes how Dalí's family influenced his early art.
- **D.** It explains Dalí's early inspirations.

4. As used in the passage, the word *eccentricity* most nearly means behavior that is
- **A.** bizarre.
- **B.** normal.
- **C.** expected.
- **D.** lunatic.

5. According to the passage, which statement is true?
- **A.** Dalí's main inspiration came from other famous artists and their works.
- **B.** Dalí was never married.
- **C.** Dalí limited his work to the canvas.
- **D.** Dalí's parents named him after his deceased brother.

6. *Answer the following question using complete sentences:*
   How are dream visions related to the subconscious?

DIRECTIONS: *Read the passage and answer the questions that follow it.*

Monstrous Mengele

JOSEF MENGELE (1911–1979) WAS A NAZI German military officer and physician during World War II. He obtained a Ph.D. from the University Munich and an M.D. in 1938 from Frankfurt University. In 1938, Mengele joined the SS, an elite unit of the Nazi party that served as Hitler's personal security force. After marrying his first wife, Irene Schoenbein, he joined several medical corps and armed units of the SS. During combat, he received awards for bravery, including the Iron Cross and the Wound Badge.

On May 24, 1943, he became the medical officer at Auschwitz, the largest Holocaust **concentration** camp, where he remained for twenty-one months. During this time, he was referred to as the "Angel of Death" for performing horrific experiments on prisoners and selecting more than 400,000 victims to die in the gas chambers. Although Mengele experimented on men, women, and children, he was fascinated with twins and often selected them to be placed in special barracks. He attempted to change children's eye color by injecting chemicals into the eyes, gave blood transfusions, removed organs, conjoined twins

together, and amputated limbs—all without anesthetics. If subjects survived his experiments, they were usually put to death and dissected for further investigation. Approximately 3,000 twins died in to his experiments. Also interested in dwarfs, Mengele had a group of seven called "his dwarf family," which underwent frequent experimentation but was also given special treatment.

In 1945, Mengele escaped Germany while dressed as a member of the infantry. He then became a hired hand on a farm and moved about Germany under various aliases. Having fled to Buenos Aires, Argentina, in the 1950s, he worked in the textile industry, drawing on business contacts from his father's company and hiding with the support of a tightly-knit group of Nazi supporters. After seeking refuge in other Latin countries, including Paraguay and Brazil, he drowned on a beach in Brazil while visiting friends in 1979. His family and friends kept his death a secret until 1985. Much to the dismay of the many who sought explanations and justice, he was never apprehended, nor was he punished for his **heinous** crimes against humanity. ◗

QUESTIONS

1. Why did the author write this passage?
   A. to describe the tragedies prisoners faced in concentration camps
   B. to explain why experimental surgeries were performed on prisoners
   C. to describe the actions of one Nazi
   D. to explain why Auschwitz had the worst reputation of all concentration camps

2. Which of the following would be the best title for this passage?
   A. Mad Scientist
   B. The Angel of Death
   C. Prisoner Experimentation
   D. The Auschwitz Angel

3. As used in the passage, the word *heinous* most nearly means
   A. horrifying.
   B. alluring.
   C. mean.
   D. unforgivable.

4. According to the passage, which statement is true?
   A. Mengele murdered hundreds of thousands of victims over the course of five years while working at Auschwitz.
   B. Mengele gave his victims painkillers during experimentation.
   C. Mengele was never tried for his crimes.
   D. The SS was a military division that battled against Hitler during WWII.

5. According to the passage, which statement is false?
   A. Mengele was married more than once.
   B. Mengele was a soldier who was rewarded for courageous battle actions.
   C. Some prisoners were given preferential treatment while at Auschwitz.
   D. Mengele performed his experiments with no scientific knowledge of the human body.

6. *Answer the following question using complete sentences:*
   What reasons could Mengele have for performing such horrible actions?

DIRECTIONS: *Read the passage and answer the questions that follow it.*

Octopush

WHILE MOST PEOPLE ENVISION the sport of hockey being played on the ice in skates or on pavement in roller blades, some athletes play underwater with snorkels. Underwater hockey, also called octopush, is a non-contact sport in which two teams compete to shoot the puck into the opponent's goal. Players attempt to maneuver the puck, called a *squid*, with *pushers* (plastic or wooden sticks, which are approximately one foot long). Athletes wear masks, fins, snorkels,

mouth guards, caps, and gloves specially designed to prevent **abrasions** and impact injuries to the playing hand. Teams are composed of ten players; however, a maximum of only six athletes from each team may compete at once. The puck is placed in the middle of the pool while players hover above their goals awaiting the start of the game. Once play begins, each athlete guards his or her assigned zone but may swim anywhere in the pool. Playing continues until one team scores a goal, or the referee signals a break, which may be the result of a foul, a timeout, or the end of the period. The game is played in two ten- to fifteen-minute halves with a half-time interval, during which teams switch sides of the pool. Since players compete under six- to eight-feet of water, the game is very much a team sport; players rely on each other to take control of the puck while others surface for air.

Invented in Britain in 1954, to keep divers in shape during the off-season, the sport now boasts international appeal for all ages. The World Underwater Federation holds world championships every two years. More than thirty-six teams, with representatives from Ireland, U.S.A., France, South Africa, and others, competing at the World Underwater Hockey Championships in Christchurch, New Zealand, in 2004. The sport continues to grow in popularity, as the many underwater hockey clubs **adhere** to a for-fun policy: they play for enjoyment. ⬤

QUESTIONS

1. **Why did the author write this passage?**
   - **A.** to explain how hockey players keep in shape during winter months
   - **B.** to describe an unconventional form of hockey
   - **C.** to inform the reader about a popular sport in Great Britain
   - **D.** to describe the World Underwater Federation

2. **Of the following statements about underwater hockey, which is true?**
   - **A.** Players may stay only in their assigned zones.
   - **B.** The game is divided into three periods.
   - **C.** Players defend specific zones in the pool.
   - **D.** A maximum of ten players from each team may be in the pool at one time.

3. **As used in the passage, the word *abrasions* most nearly means**
   - **A.** irritations.
   - **B.** scrapes.
   - **C.** fractures.
   - **D.** bruises.

4. **Using the information provided in the passage, which statement is the most logical inference?**
   - **A.** Because the sport is non-contact, players may compete against different age groups and weight classes.
   - **B.** Because octopush is played in water, it is not as fast as regular hockey or as difficult to play.
   - **C.** Since players are allowed to wear snorkels, it is not essential for athletes to hold their breath for long periods of time.
   - **D.** Underwater hockey is popular only in English-speaking countries.

5. **Which of the following best states the reason for the first paragraph?**
   - **A.** It describes how octopush got its name.
   - **B.** It describes the rules of underwater hockey.
   - **C.** It describes how athletes train during the off-season.
   - **D.** It explains how athletes compete in octopush.

6. *Answer the following question using complete sentences:*
   Octopush is not a commonly televised sport. What factors might make viewing a game of octopush difficult? Explain.

DIRECTIONS: *Read the passage and answer the questions that follow it.*

Abelard and Heloise

THE TRUE ROMANTIC STORY of Abelard and Heloise reveals one of history's most tragic love affairs. Heloise was a beautiful and well-educated woman who lived in France during the twelfth century. Her uncle, Notre Dame's Canon Fulbert, hired Peter Abelard, a well-known philosopher, as her tutor. Although Abelard was twenty years her senior, they fell madly in love. After Heloise became pregnant, she feared her uncle's **reprisal** and worried about Abelard's reputation and social position, since teachers in the church were to sworn to celibacy. Abelard was a highly respected, talented teacher, and if news about his affair or his marriage spread, he would no longer be permitted to teach.

Although Fulbert arranged a secret marriage between the couple, Heloise believed her uncle would take greater action. She was right. In an effort to completely sever ties between the two, Fulbert violently attacked Abelard, who consequently became a monk. Heloise took refuge in a convent and gave their child to Abelard's sister. For years, their only correspondence occurred through letters filled with passion. Heloise's writings express a great yearning for their past love and closeness and an overwhelming sense of hypocrisy for entering a convent under such conditions. She wrote, "While I am denied your presence, give me at least through your words—of which you have enough and to spare—some sweet semblance of yourself...I beg you, think what you owe me, give ear to my pleas, and I will finish a long letter with a brief ending: farewell, my only love."

Abelard responded to her pleas as such, "If since our conversion from the world to God I have not yet written you any word of comfort or advice, it must not be attributed to indifference on my part but to your own good sense..." He implied that her intellect was strong enough that he need not verbalize his feelings, that she fully understood them. As time passed, Heloise accepted that Abelard would not **reciprocate** romantic discourse through his letters, so she proceeded to discusses religious matters with him, especially those surrounding the role of women within the clergy and the restrictions patriarchal society placed on women.

Although these two were deeply in love, their reliance and closeness were severed, and despite the intensity of their written communication, they never saw each other again. Today, their remains reportedly rest side-by-side at Pére Lachaise cemetery in France. ●

QUESTIONS

1. Which of the following best states the purpose of this passage?
- **A.** to describe the love affair between members of the clergy
- **B.** to explain why people should only become romantically involved with people their own age
- **C.** to inform the reader about the roles of nuns within the church
- **D.** to recite the tale of a couple tragically separated

2. Why were Abelard and Heloise married secretly?
- **A.** Teachers were not permitted to be married.
- **B.** Fulbert wanted to punish Abelard for his actions.
- **C.** Heloise could not join the convent if she were married.
- **D.** Heloise was too young to be married.

3. What is the purpose of the first paragraph?
- **A.** It describes how Abelard and Heloise fell in love.
- **B.** It explains the obligations Abelard had to his career.
- **C.** It describes Fulbert's role in their separation.
- **D.** It shows how pregnancy out-of-wedlock affected women in previous centuries.

4. According to the passage, which statement is true?
- **A.** Heloise was twenty years older than Abelard.
- **B.** Abelard's and Heloise's bodies are buried a great distance from one another.
- **C.** Fulbert was appeased by the marriage and sought no further actions against Abelard.
- **D.** Abelard's sister raised Abelard and Heloise's child.

5. As used in the passage, the word *reciprocate* most nearly means
- **A.** reenact.
- **B.** forget.
- **C.** return.
- **D.** acknowledge.

6. Why did Abelard become a monk?
- **A.** He was a teacher of the Church, and his next logical step was to enter the monastery.
- **B.** Fulbert's attack most likely influenced him to choose a life away from Heloise.
- **C.** Once Heloise joined a convent, he realized they would never be together again and became a monk.
- **D.** Fulbert forced him to enter the monastery.

DIRECTIONS: *Read the passage and answer the questions that follow it.*

Gladiators

ALTHOUGH MODERN SOCIETY glamorizes gladiators for their strength and bravery, most gladiators arrived in the arena by force, not at all as a result of their own desire to prove their strength and aptitude. Gladiators, mostly criminals, slaves, or prisoners of war, were brought by their owners, called a *lanistas*, to combat each other and wild animals in arenas merely for the morbid entertainment of ancient Romans. Professional gladiators, on the other hand, were volunteers who participated in the games as a means of making a living and were often very popular with the crowds. Gladiators gained immediate status, even though they would leave the arena to resume their role as slaves to their *lanistas*. They were often **revered** for their loyalty, courage, and discipline. Although most gladiators were men, women were permitted to combat in the arena. It is known that Septimius Severus, who ruled Rome from 193 to 211 A.D., allowed female gladiators but banned the practice in 200 A.D. Outfitted in the armor and weaponry of non-Romans, the gladiators played the role of Rome's enemies. The gladiators would dress in a specific enemy's garb and attempt to reenact famous battles. Gladiator battles were also held for religious ceremonies and to celebrate the death of an influential person.

Gladiators' fighting styles varied depending on their rank. For example, criminals condemned for capital crimes fought without weapons. Some gladiators trained at special schools, called *laudi*, to learn combat techniques that allowed them to disable and capture their opponents. Gladiators who trained at these schools fought with their choice of weapons and armor. During training, gladiators received three meals a day and medical attention when necessary. They were paid for each battle they fought and could earn their freedom if they survived three to five years of combat; however, most did not survive, even though they were required to fight only a few times per year.

After an **opponent** was wounded, the crowd would shout, "*habet, hoc habet*," meaning "he has had it." As a cry for mercy, the wounded one would extend a finger on the raised left hand and await the verdict. If the decision was death, the defeated would grasp his conqueror's thigh and await a fatal slaying. Attendants dressed as the ferryman Charon and the god Mercury would attend to the body. Mercury poked the body with a hot iron to make sure the defeated was indeed dead after Charon struck the body with a hammer. The victor received a reward, usually made of gold, and a palm leaf symbolizing victory. ●

QUESTIONS

1. Which of the following best states the truth about gladiators?
   A. Most were members of the military.
   B. Most enjoyed high status and were free men.
   C. Most were volunteers who sought glory.
   D. Most were there against their wishes.

2. What would be a good title for this passage?
   A. Gory Days of Battle
   B. Battling for Rome
   C. Glory of Gladiators
   D. Morbid Men

3. Which best describes the reason for the final paragraph?
   A. It explains the ultimate result of gladiator battle.
   B. It describes the role of the crowd during the battle.
   C. It explains how gladiators fought against each other.
   D. It demonstrates the religious significance of gladiator battle.

4. As used in the passage, the word *revered* most nearly means
   A. worshipped.
   B. respected.
   C. feared.
   D. rewarded.

5. According to the passage, which statement is true?
   A. Gladiators wore enemy attire.
   B. Only volunteer gladiators received training.
   C. The battles of gladiators bore no religious significance.
   D. All gladiators were men.

6. *Answer the following question using complete sentences:*
   Why did the gladiators not wear the armor of the Roman military?

DIRECTIONS: *Read the passage and answer the questions that follow it.*

Jellyfish

JELLYFISH ARE FREE-SWIMMING **inverte-brate** animals that can be found in every oceanic body. While not biologically categorized as fish, they are classified in the phylum Cnidaria and classes Hydrozoa and Scyphozoa. Jellyfish are composed of approximately ninety-five percent water. A jellyfish's body, which resembles an umbrella or bell, is composed of an upper layer, the epidermis, and a lower layer, called the gastrodermis. A **gelatinous** material, called *mesoglea*, fills the space between the two layers, giving the jellyfish its gel-like consistency. Tentacles, also called oral arms, are suspended from the bottom of the jellyfish's internal structure on most species and are covered with stinging cells, called *cnidocytes*. The injected toxins from the tentacles can cause reactions in humans ranging from minor irritation to death, depending on the species and the poisons produced. Many jellyfish are brightly colored, and their internal structures are visible through the bell. Depending on the species, jellyfish can range from less than an inch to more than five feet in diameter.

Jellyfish move vertically by contracting and relaxing the bell muscles and are carried horizontally by waves and ocean currents. Sometimes they travel in groups, called smacks, or congregate in massive swarms, called blooms. Because a jellyfish lacks basic sensory organs and a brain, it uses its nervous systems and sensory structures, called *rhopalia*, to perceive stimuli. Jellyfish also lack a respiratory system; however, the thin layer of epidermis allows oxygen to be absorbed and carbon dioxide to be expelled. A jellyfish catches its prey using its cnidocytes to stun or kill other animals before using the tentacles to carry the food to its mouth, which is located in the center of its undersurface. Once food passes through the mouth, it then enters the stomach and is distributed through the body via radial canals. Because a jellyfish's digestive system is incomplete, the same orifice is used for both food intake and waste expulsion. Although this seems rather disgusting, it is a perfectly efficient system for the jellyfish, which has become quite a popular attraction at aquariums around the world. ●

QUESTIONS

1. How does the jellyfish breathe?
   A. Oxygen passes through its cnidocytes.
   B. Oxygen passes through its mesoglea.
   C. Oxygen passes through its epidermis.
   D. Oxygen passes through its mouth.

2. Which of the following best states the purpose of the first paragraph?
   A. It describes the mesoglea.
   B. It informs the reader about the composition of jellyfish.
   C. It explains where jellyfish can be found.
   D. It informs the reader about the functions and dangers of the tentacles.

3. According to the passage, which statement is true?
   A. Jellyfish have a central nervous system.
   B. The sting of some jellyfish can kill a human.
   C. Jellyfish have digestive systems similar to humans.
   D. Approximately one-half of jellyfish have tentacles.

4. As used in the passage, the word *gelatinous* most nearly means
   A. runny.
   B. sticky.
   C. foamy.
   D. jelly.

5. Which of the following would be the best title for this passage?
   A. Gelatinous Jellyfish
   B. Jellyfish, a Marine Mammal
   C. Blooming Jellyfish
   D. Swimming with Danger

6. According to the passage, which organ is found in a jellyfish?
   A. brain
   B. stomach
   C. eyes
   D. gills

DIRECTIONS: *Read the passage and answer the questions that follow it.*

Sweatshops

SWEATSHOPS AROUND THE WORLD today owe their existence to an economic system that demands lower costs and higher profits while encouraging **globalization**. As industry becomes more global, and more companies continue to outsource work to other countries, the prevalence of sweatshops continues to grow. Corporations increase their profits by contracting work to foreign manufacturers. The contractors produce goods cheaply by making laborers work long hours under poor and unsafe conditions for inadequate pay and few or no benefits while suffering various abuses at the hands of their employers. Essentially, this is the exploitation of people who work in such shops out of necessity, for most people would not work under such conditions if they had a choice. In many sweatshops, laborers are children and victims of dire poverty, people who desperately need the income and are forced by this need to accept what work they can find. Many companies claim that outsourcing work to developing countries does the consumer a great service by keeping prices low. Sadly, while companies reap higher profits and consumers enjoy cheaper prices, farmers, workers, families, and the environment suffer.

The disparity is high between the pay rates of corporate executives and those of the shop workers. According to *Sweatshop Watch*, workers in the garment industry make approximately one percent of the garment's sale price, and many workers earn wages significantly below minimum wage. Those in Pakistan, for example, average twenty-three cents per hour, while those in Mexico earn one dollar and seventy-five cents. Most of the money consumers pay for garments ends up feeding the corporations' advertising and executive payroll budgets. Workers at a prominent blue jean factory in Saipan (a U.S. commonwealth in the Pacific) were receiving three dollars and five cents per hour while the CEO of the company made almost 4000 times that amount.

Some supporters argue that sweatshop work is better than no work at all. In reality, the manufacturer is taking advantage of these people, and the money they receive does little to improve their economic situation. Children often work in sweatshops alongside their parents because there is nowhere else for them to go. They gain no education and have no means to secure training for a better-paying job elsewhere. The cycle of poverty and exploitive labor continues. Sweatshops can be stopped, however. Courts have become involved, as lawsuits have been filed against sweatshops that abuse their labor force. Many consumers have expressed disdain for sweatshops and are willing to pay more for goods they know were not made in sweatshops. By **boycotting** goods of manufactures that utilize sweatshops and pressuring companies to change, consumers can help stop the mistreatment of workers. ◗

QUESTIONS

1. **Which of the following best states the author's purpose?**
    A. to inform the reader about outsourcing
    B. to explain how some major corporations exploit workers
    C. to describe how harmful large corporations are to workers
    D. to inform the reader about the history of sweatshops

2. **Which of the following would the most logical conclusion drawn from the second paragraph?**
    A. If companies discontinued the use of sweatshops, the problem would be solved.
    B. If companies reduced executive salaries and reduced the number of sweat shop employees, they would realize greater profits.
    C. If companies discontinued their outsourcing policies and used only American labor, the problem of sweatshop labor would dissipate.
    D. If companies reduced advertising and executive payroll budgets, they could increase workers' wages and still realize a profit.

3. **Which of the following best describes the reason for the second paragraph?**
    A. It shows how much money brand labels can cost consumers.
    B. It demonstrates the pay discrepancy between laborers in foreign countries.
    C. It highlights the low wages of sweatshop workers in comparison to those of executives.
    D. It describes the excessive pay of sweatshop laborers in comparison to executives' pay.

4. **According to the passage, which statement is most accurate?**
    A. Sweatshops are necessary to keep prices low in the U.S.
    B. Consumers cannot control or help curb the actions of corporations.
    C. Sweatshop laborers endure physical, emotional, and mental abuses.
    D. Consumers do not care about the victimization of foreign laborers.

5. **As used in the passage, the word *boycotting* most nearly means**
    A. destroying.
    B. refusing.
    C. purchasing.
    D. supporting.

6. **According to the passage, which statement is false?**
    A. Sweatshops are used to cut costs for manufacturers.
    B. Sweatshops often employ children as laborers.
    C. Sweatshops are the result of greed and negligence.
    D. Sweatshops are only found in third world countries.

DIRECTIONS: *Read the passage and answer the questions that follow it.*

Tea

Since ancient times in China, a series of customs and rituals has surrounded the preparation and consumption of tea. In China, tea is appropriate for any occasion, consumed regularly in both casual and formal situations. Socially, the serving of tea demonstrates respect. A person in a **subordinate** position may acknowledge authority by preparing or serving tea; for example, a child may serve his or her elders, or an employee may serve his or her boss. Drinking tea with relatives on Sunday is incredibly popular in China, and is considered a way to unite generations and share each other's company. Pouring tea for a person whom you have wronged is interpreted as an apology and a sign of regret. At a wedding, tea plays an important role for the couple and the families. During the ceremony, the bride and groom offer tea to their parents, symbolically displaying gratitude for their nurturing and care. As part of the celebration, the families express their acceptance and unity by drinking tea.

The Chinese, having used tea since ancient times, have developed a particular method for brewing the beverage. While the methods may vary depending on the occasion or type of tea, preparing tea in China is a serious endeavor, performed precisely, almost as though it were an art form. Typically, the teapot is first rinsed with hot water; then, leaves are added to fill one-third of the pot. The pot is then filled halfway with boiling water and drained immediately to rinse the leaves. Hot water is added again to steep the leaves. It is important not to allow bubbles to enter the mixture, which should not **mull** any longer than thirty seconds. The tea is served within one minute; each cup is expected to have the same color, flavor, and aroma. The excess tea is poured into another pot to keep the infusion period short. It is possible to brew five or six rounds of tea from a single pot of leaves. Although this is the traditional Chinese method of brewing, other cultures indulge in this process, as well. ●

QUESTIONS

1. **Why does the passage explain that tea is both an apology and a sign of regret?**
   - **A.** The author is pointing out that tea represents regret; therefore tea is suitable for this occasion.
   - **B.** The author is emphasizing the sincerity of an apology accompanied by regret.
   - **C.** The author made a mistake, and this is an example of redundant wording.
   - **D.** The author is using this example to support the thesis that tea has one important social meaning.

2. **Which of the following would be the best title for this passage?**
   - **A.** Chinese Teas
   - **B.** Tea: A Way of Life
   - **C.** Brewing Tea
   - **D.** Tea: World's Most Popular Beverage

3. **According to the passage, which of the following is celebrated with tea?**
   - **A.** admiration
   - **B.** power
   - **C.** sympathy
   - **D.** scandal

4. **As used in the passage, the word *subordinate* most nearly means**
   - **A.** senior.
   - **B.** superior.
   - **C.** inferior.
   - **D.** intimidating.

5. **Which of the following statements best describes the process for brewing tea?**
   - **A.** Boiling water is added directly to a teapot previously filled with leaves.
   - **B.** A teapot is filled with leaves and water before the mixture is boiled for thirty seconds.
   - **C.** To ensure consistent color, flavor, and aroma, leaves are covered with boiling water and allowed to infuse for several minutes before being poured.
   - **D.** The teapot is cleaned and the leaves are rinsed before being allowed to infuse for a short period.

6. *Answer the following question using complete sentences:*
   How might serving tea demonstrate respect?

DIRECTIONS: *Read the passage and answer the questions that follow it.*

Catalina de Erauso

HISTORY HAS RECORDED many women who abandoned their traditional feminine **garb** and took on a masculine identity in order to gain rights and live freely. Among them is the remarkable Catalina de Erauso, who was born around the year 1585, in San Sebastian's Basque region, which lay between northern Spain and France. Catalina's parents sent her to a convent to be raised in her faith and ultimately become a nun, as was the custom. The day before she was to take her final vows, she had an **altercation** with one of the nuns and fled the convent where she had lived since she was four. To disguise herself as a man, she cut her hair and made a new wardrobe. Although she was only fifteen when she left, she was able to support herself by working for various people, on ships, and in the military under the name Antonio de Erauso.

She traveled throughout Spain working different jobs for three years before leaving for the New World. As a soldier, she received the name "La Monja Alférez" (The Second Lieutenant Nun) and participated in wars against natives of Chile, Argentina, and Peru. She fought and killed men of various ranks, including soldiers, officers, and bureaucrats who threatened her "honor as a man."

In an evening duel, she accidentally killed her own brother. Although she fled a permanent life with the church, she often sought refuge from enemies by taking sanctuary in its buildings.

For twenty years, La Monja Alférez continued to live life as a man, gambling, fighting, and consequently killing in self-defense, when necessary, throughout Spain and the New World. It was not until she had been badly wounded in a fight that she revealed her true identity to the bishop of Guamanga. After receiving a life pension from the king for her military service, she cloistered herself again and lived in a convent for two years. Pope Urban VII gave her permission to continue living as a man since she was still virtuous and had served Spain. Considering that this was the early 1600s, and Catholicism had strict rules about gender roles, it is remarkable that such permission was granted. Although the exact reason for the Pope's consent is unclear, it is likely that her cross-dressing was considered a means of ridding herself of her inferior status as a woman. She had proven her desire to be superior; therefore, she was deemed worthy of dressing as a man, which she continued to do until her death in 1650. ❍

QUESTIONS

1. Which of the following best states the author's purpose?
   A. to describe how women lived in Spain during the 1600s
   B. to inform the reader about a woman who spent much of her life pretending to be a man
   C. to explain how a woman could abandon the church and still be religious
   D. to inform the reader about the limitations of gender roles in Spanish society during the 1600s

2. Why did Catalina pretend to be a man?
   A. She wanted to become part of the king's court.
   B. This was the only way she could enroll in the military and fight for her country.
   C. She was rebelling against her parents.
   D. This afforded her freedoms that were not typically given to women.

3. Which of the following statements best describes Catalina de Erauso?
   A. She was a heretic who used the church only when it suited her.
   B. She fought for her country as a soldier.
   C. She was a thief and a cross dresser.
   D. She gambled, murdered ruthlessly, and wrestled with her identity crisis.

4. As used in the passage, the word *altercation* most nearly means
   A. meeting.
   B. brawl.
   C. quarrel.
   D. duel.

5. According to the passage, which statement is true?
   A. Catalina de Erauso was a murderer and gambler.
   B. Catalina de Erauso lived as a man in order to hide from the law.
   C. Catalina de Erauso had no use for the Church after discarding her habit.
   D. Catalina de Erauso lived as a nun longer than she lived as a man.

6. *Answer the following question using complete sentences:*
   If Pope Urban VII granted Catalina's request to live as a man during the 1600s, why is cross-dressing still frowned upon today by various religions and society as a whole?

DIRECTIONS: *Read the passage and answer the questions that follow it.*

Arnold Schwarzenegger

ARNOLD SCHWARZENEGGER WAS BORN on July 30, 1947, in Thal, Austria. Although his father, a police chief and former Nazi storm trooper, wanted him to become a soccer player, he preferred bodybuilding. He earned the nickname "the Austrian Oak" after winning the Mr. Europe junior title in 1965. The bodybuilder won many amateur, professional, and international competitions, including five Mr. Universe titles and seven Mr. Olympia titles. He traveled to the U.S.

for exhibitions, attended college here, and graduated from the University of Wisconsin with a degree in business and economics. Then, he opened his own bodybuilding equipment company and became a millionaire by the age of twenty-two. He became a U.S. citizen in 1983. Schwarzenegger married television broadcaster Maria Shriver, the niece of former President John F. Kennedy, in 1986.

Schwarzenegger used his **physique** to enter the film industry, taking roles as bodybuilders and muscle-bound heroes. Although his hit movie *Conan the Barbarian* (1982) made him instantly famous, he is perhaps best known for his roles and catch phrases in the *Terminator* series. After starring with Danny De Vito in *Twins* (1988), Schwarzenegger proved he was capable of performing comedic roles and taking on deeper dimensions as an actor, although not all of Schwarzenegger's films have resulted in blockbuster hits.

As a guest on *The Tonight Show with Jay Leno* in August of 2003, Schwarzenegger announced he would run for governor of California. Although he is a Republican, he claims to be socially **moderate** by taking a pro-choice stance and supporting some gay rights issues. On November 17, 2003, he was sworn-in to replace Gray Davis after winning a recall election. He has announced that he will run for reelection in 2006. He has hinted at wanting to become President; however, since the Constitution requires the president to be native born, Schwarzenegger, a naturalized citizen, cannot hold the office. ◗

QUESTIONS

1. Which of the following best describes Arnold Schwarzenegger?

    A. persistent, greedy, admired

    B. determined, educated, successful

    C. indifferent, talented, introverted

    D. selfless, humorous, reclusive

2. What would be a good title for this passage?

    A. Mr. Olympia

    B. Schwarzenegger for President

    C. Bodybuilder, Actor, Politician

    D. Governor of California

3. Which of the following best states the reason for the final paragraph?

    A. It informs the reader about his affiliation with the Republican Party.

    B. It describes his political achievements and aspirations.

    C. It highlights some of his political views.

    D. It explains how he got into politics.

4. As used in the passage, the word *moderate* most nearly means

    A. balanced.

    B. fair.

    C. conservative.

    D. liberal.

5. According to the passage, which statement is true?

    A. Schwarzenegger earned most of his money by marrying into the Kennedy family.

    B. Schwarzenegger has won the title of Mr. Universe seven times.

    C. Schwarzenegger announced his gubernatorial candidacy on late night television.

    D. Schwarzenegger used his political connections to break into Hollywood.

6. *Answer the following question using complete sentences:*
Why might the Constitution not allow naturalized citizens to become president?

DIRECTIONS: *Read the passage and answer the questions that follow it.*

Queen of the Nile

ALTHOUGH THERE WERE many other Cleopatras before her, Cleopatra Thea Philopator VII (69 B.C.–30 B.C.) was the queen of ancient Egypt and the last member of the Ptolemaic dynasty. Her name literally means "the Goddess Cleopatra, the beloved of Her Father." At the age of seventeen, Cleopatra married her younger brother, Ptolemy XII, and co-ruled ancient Egypt after the death of their father. As a female, Cleopatra should have been subordinate to her brother; however, she removed his name from official documents and permitted only her face to be stamped on coins. Because of her rebellious behavior, Cleopatra was forced to flee her country. With the assistance of Julius Caesar, Cleopatra revolted against her brother and won the kingdom, which still belonged to Rome. After her husband/brother drowned in the Nile, she married Ptolemy XIII. However, she quickly became Caesar's mistress and followed him to Rome. While in Rome, Cleopatra bore Caesar's son, Caesarion, whom Caesar refused to make heir.

After Caesar was **assassinated**, Cleopatra and Caesarion returned to Egypt. After the death of Ptolemy XIV, Cleopatra regained the throne and co-reigned with her son. Mark Antony, a ruler of Rome, visited Cleopatra in 42 B.C., to question her loyalty. Antony, having fallen madly in love with her, spent the winter in Alexandria with her. Realizing her potential to regain power in Egypt, Cleopatra aligned herself with Mark Antony when he visited four years later, and married him in 36 B.C. She became the co-ruler of Egypt and Cyprus and received the title "Queen of Kings."

Hating and fearing Cleopatra, many Romans sought to end the lives of the couple. Octavian, a prominent Roman soldier and future emperor, was able to convince the **Senate** to wage war against Egypt. After losing the battle of Actium, Octavian invaded Egypt. Soon after Octavian's arrival, Antony fell purposefully on his own sword, and Cleopatra poisoned herself when faced against Octavian, who had murdered Caesarion.

Cleopatra's story is a fascinating one: throughout history, relatively few women have possessed the same degree of power, persistence, and fame. Her story has been portrayed by classic playwrights and modern filmmakers, alike, and will likely be the focus of many yet to come. ◗

QUESTIONS

1. Which of the following best states the author's purpose?

    A. to inform the reader about famous marriages in ancient Egypt

    B. to explain how Cleopatra made history

    C. to describe the ruling practices of Cleopatra

    D. to explain how ancient Egypt was ruled by queens

2. What prompted Mark Antony's first visit to Cleopatra?

    A. Antony wanted to test Cleopatra's loyalty to Rome.

    B. Octavian sent Antony to secure Egypt.

    C. Antony had fallen madly in love with Cleopatra.

    D. Cleopatra had invited him to observe her government.

3. Which of the following best states the reason for the first paragraph?

    A. It describes how royalty married only within the family.

    B. It informs the reader about Cleopatra's family life.

    C. It explains how Cleopatra lost and regained the throne of Egypt.

    D. It describes how important Caesar was to Cleopatra's reign.

4. According to the passage, which statement is true?

    A. Antony and Cleopatra committed suicide.

    B. Egypt was never ruled under another country during Cleopatra's reign.

    C. Ptolemy XIII was Cleopatra's brother and first husband.

    D. Cleopatra had no children.

5. As used in the passage, the word *Senate* most nearly means

    A. kingdom.

    B. government.

    C. peasants.

    D. armies.

6. Which group of words best describes Cleopatra?

    A. unknown, powerful, fearful

    B. feared, subordinate, wise

    C. manipulative, fragile, royal

    D. clever, feared, powerful

DIRECTIONS: *Read the passage and answer the questions that follow it.*

Two Women and a Pirate Ship

When most people hear the word *pirates*, they imagine violent, unkempt, ruthless sailors who attacked and plundered ships mercilessly. Very rarely do people picture the two toughest women to threaten the high seas: Anne Bonny and Mary Read.

Born out of wedlock in Ireland in the late seventeenth century, Anne Cormac endured a rather turbulent childhood, eventually relocating with her parents to America. Although her father became a successful plantation owner, Anne ran away when he disapproved of her choice of husband, James Bonny, a pirate. Anne and James sailed for New Providence. There, she grew disenchanted with James and took up piracy with Jack Rackham, otherwise known as Calico Jack for his colorful garb. When James pled to the governor to reclaim his wife, Jack offered money to keep Anne, which was allowable by law at the time. Anne refused the offer, and was sentenced to be beaten and returned to her husband. Instead, she disguised herself as a man and fled with Jack on his ship, the *Revenge*.

Meanwhile, Mary Read, the daughter of a widow, spent her childhood in England disguised as a boy, probably to inherit her father's business. Eventually, Mary was forced to find work and joined the military. Shortly thereafter, she fell in love with a fellow soldier. After revealing her true identity, she married the man. When he passed away, Mary once again dressed as a man and sailed for the West Indies. It was here that her ship was attacked by the *Revenge*. Mary, whom Calico Jack and his crew thought was a man, was given a choice: perish or join the crew. She chose the latter.

Anne and Mary developed a reputation as being pitiless and strong; however, they both had to continue disguising themselves as men. It was a dangerous time for a woman to be at sea, pirate or not, and although Anne and Mary were capable of **emerging** victorious from many a duel and attack, they did not want to invite unnecessary attention. Anne, Mary, and Jack enjoyed their infamy and the fear they inspired for only a few years before they were captured and tried for piracy, bringing an end to their **reign** in the Caribbean. ●

QUESTIONS

1. The author wrote this passage to inform the reader about

    A. piracy in the Caribbean.

    B. two female pirates.

    C. Calico Jack.

    D. Anne Bonny's life.

2. Why did Mary dress as a boy in her childhood?

    A. to be eligible for an education

    B. to be eligible to join the military

    C. to be eligible for male privileges

    D. to be eligible to own a home

3. How did Mary come to work on Calico Jack's ship?

    A. She was captured while pretending to be a man.

    B. She arrived in New Providence and joined the crew.

    C. She was kidnapped by pirates and traded to Jack.

    D. She became a pirate when her husband died.

4. As used in the passage, *emerging* most nearly means

    A. opening.

    B. explaining.

    C. fighting.

    D. finishing.

5. Why did Mary and Anne continue to disguise their identities?

    A. They did not want the crew of the *Revenge* to know they were women.

    B. Revealing their true identities would attract dangerous attention.

    C. Their husbands were searching for them, and the women had to hide their identities.

    D. Anne and Mary would not be able to fight in women's clothing.

6. Which of the following groups of words best describes Anne and Mary?

    A. delicate, pitiless, brutal

    B. false, strong, domestic

    C. heroic, pitiless, feminine

    D. brave, brutal, strong

DIRECTIONS: *Read the passage and answer the questions that follow it.*

Alexander the Great

ALEXANDER THE GREAT, also known as Alexander III, was born in July of 356 B.C. Aristotle, the famous philosopher, was the tutor who provided Alexander with a classic education. Alexander took the throne after the assassination of his father, Philip II, in 336 B.C., and became the king of Macedon at the age of twenty. After securing Greece and the Balkan Peninsula, Alexander, as the head of the Greek army, waged war on Persia in 334 B.C. While overtaking most of Asia Minor, he

spread Greek ideals and philosophies. Alexander's vision was to conquer the entire Persian Empire. After taking command of Syria in 332 B.C., he entered Egypt and founded the city of Alexandria. He ultimately conquered all of what is present-day Afghanistan and northern India. He led men through deserts of modern-day southern Afghanistan and southern Iraq.

Alexander was known for his harsh treatment and authoritarian style. Many became angry with him for dressing in Persian attire, encouraging **tolerance**, and forcing his officers to marry Persian women. Because he demanded to be treated as a god, civilizations adopted various names for him, such as "the **accursed** Alexander" and "the two-horned one." While planning a voyage to Arabia in 323, he became ill and died at the age of thirty-three in Babylon. His son, Alexander Aegus, was born to his wife Roxana, a Bactrian princess, after Alexander's death. It is possible that Alexander the Great planned to build a worldwide empire, having conquered civilizations from Greece to India. Although he was the most successful military commander in world history, he was not successful in governing the lands he conquered. Numerous legends of his fascinating life and tactics, including tales of his birth and battlefield escapades, live on through many novels and films. ◗

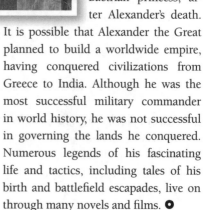

QUESTIONS

1. Which of the following best states the author's purpose?
- **A.** to inform the reader about an ancient military leader
- **B.** to explain why Alexander III was so great
- **C.** to describe ancient Greek lifestyles under the rule of Alexander the Great
- **D.** to inform the reader about battlefield techniques of ancient

2. Which of the following would be the best title for this passage?
- **A.** Alexander's Great Government
- **B.** The Quest for World Suppression
- **C.** The Downfall of Ancient Civilizations
- **D.** Alexander's Conquests

3. Which of the following best states the reason for the first paragraph?
- **A.** It describes how Alexander III became king.
- **B.** It compares Alexander's reign to other leaders of the time.
- **C.** It mentions the lands Alexander was able to conquer.
- **D.** It describes the geography of the Persian Empire.

4. As used in the passage, the word *accursed* most nearly means
- **A.** sacred.
- **B.** vengeful.
- **C.** profane.
- **D.** detestable.

5. According to the passage, which statement is true?
- **A.** Alexander the Great did not allow people of different races to intermarry.
- **B.** A city in Egypt is named after Alexander.
- **C.** Soldiers appreciated Alexander's merciful ways on the battlefield.
- **D.** Alexander was able to conquer multiple lands and govern them successfully.

6. *Answer the following question using complete sentences:*
Why would such world domination not be possible today?

DIRECTIONS: *Read the passage and answer the questions that follow it.*

AIDS

ACQUIRED IMMUNODEFICIENCY SYNDROME (AIDS) is a fatal disease caused by the human immunodeficiency virus (HIV). HIV attacks the body's white blood cells, such as the CD-4 and T cells, which fight diseases that invade the body. Once these cells are destroyed, the immune system becomes weak and prone to various infections and diseases. HIV can progress to AIDS once the immune cell count drops below 200. The virus is transmitted through the exchange of bodily fluids or through the use of infected needles. Since its discovery in 1981, AIDS has become a worldwide **pandemic** that affects tens of millions of people.

Today, Sub-Saharan Africa has the highest population of people affected by HIV and AIDS. By the end of 2005, 25.8 million people were infected, with 3.1 million new cases that year alone. With the high incidence and prevalence of the virus, more than 17 million children have become orphans in Africa. Countries in Africa are affected by the virus at varied rates. For example, the prevalence of adults in Somalia with the virus is less than two percent, while it affects over thirty-eight percent of the adult population in Swaziland. In general, areas in southern Africa have the highest rate of infection while western Africa has the lowest. The effects of the virus have impacted many aspects of society, including education, industry, agriculture, health systems, and the economy. Most people infected with the virus are between the ages of fifteen and forty-nine, which are also the prime working years. This has caused a **degression** in progress, the devastation of entire communities, and a lowered average life expectancy.

It is inevitable that the number of infected people will continue to grow since there is no cure for the virus. However, preventative measures are proving to be effective. Education, including awareness campaigns and prevention programs, has shown to aid in decreasing the rate of HIV incidence in parts of Africa. Massive efforts, such as providing education, testing, counseling, and supplying medications, are still needed to bring this disease under control while researchers work for a cure. ●

QUESTIONS

1. Which of the following best states the author's purpose?

   A. to inform the reader about how the AIDS virus can be contracted

   B. to explain why Africa is the highest population affected with AIDS

   C. to inform the reader about the prevalence of AIDS in Africa

   D. to describe the efforts taken to stop the AIDS pandemic

2. Why is AIDS such a problem for society today?

   A. It is a pandemic.

   B. The disease continues to spread because there is no cure.

   C. There are no education programs to prevent transmission of the disease.

   D. It causes HIV.

3. What is the purpose of the final paragraph?

   A. It explains how the spread of HIV can be prevented.

   B. It informs the reader about how AIDS can be treated.

   C. It demonstrates the ways in which HIV will continue to escalate.

   D. It shows that there is nothing that can be done to stop the virus from spreading.

4. According to the passage, which statement is true?

   A. AIDS causes HIV.

   B. Countries in western Africa have the highest prevalence of the virus.

   C. Millions of children have become orphaned due to parents dying from AIDS.

   D. HIV can be contracted through casual contact with an infected person.

5. As used in the passage, the word *degression* most nearly means

   A. expansion.

   B. facilitation.

   C. mutation.

   D. reversion.

6. Which of the following best states the reason for the second paragraph?

   A. It proves AIDS is a problem for foreign countries such as Africa.

   B. It shows how the prevalence of AIDS impacts infected societies as a whole.

   C. It provides statistics about the prevalence of the virus.

   D. It informs the reader about the health consequences of AIDS.

DIRECTIONS: *Read the passage and answer the questions that follow it.*

The Road to Atlantis

IT IS VERY LIKELY THAT Plato, an ancient Greek teacher and philosopher, fabricated the legendary island-continent called Atlantis. According to Plato's tale, the city of Atlantis was the creation of Poseidon, and its inhabitants became strong and prosperous, developed advanced laws, and enjoyed thriving success—until **corruption** and greed overtook the ruling class. Unhappy with the state of affairs on the island, the gods destroyed Atlantis with a massive earthquake, sinking the island, leaving no remains. The story was a lesson about human nature and living morally. Most likely, the story was just that: a work of fiction. Many people, however, have made it a mission to find this elusive land.

Atlantis has become a fascinating **enigma**. From treasure-hunters to scientists, countless people have hunted for evidence of the mythical land. According to Plato's account, it was located west of Gibraltar in the Atlantic Ocean; however, more recently, scientists have suggested that Plato was referring to the island of Crete in the Mediterranean. In the 1600s B.C., the Thera eruption on nearby Santorini essentially devastated the island of Crete, dispelling its inhabitants, the Minoans, whose impressive rule and flourishing culture ceased rather abruptly within 200 years of the eruption.

Yet more believers continue to search around the world for the legendary city of Atlantis. The discovery of the Bimini Road in the Bahamas islands has inspired an entire generation of explorers. Imaginative minds believe this J-shaped underwater rock formation is a road to Atlantis, even though scientists have proven it to be naturally-occurring, eroded beachrock. Scientific findings do not sway these die-hard Atlantis seekers. They continue to explore, dig, and search for any clues, any piece of evidence, no matter how minute, that might just prove the existence of Plato's phantom creation.❍

QUESTIONS

1. According to Plato, what happened to the city of Atlantis?

    A. It never reached thriving success.

    B. It was destroyed by a volcanic eruption.

    C. It was raided by Minoan ships.

    D. It was destroyed by an earthquake.

2. What lesson might Plato have been trying to teach through his story of Atlantis?

    A. Greed tends to anger those around you.

    B. Moral and selfless values build success.

    C. Success should be highly valued, but prosperity is more important.

    D. You should work hard to please those who help you.

3. Why does the author mention the island of Crete?

    A. to show that the Altantians were related to the Minoans

    B. to show that Plato did not know his geography

    C. to show that the story may be based on a real event

    D. to show that Atlantis was destroyed by a volcanic eruption

4. According to the passage, which of the following has been scientifically proven?

    A. The Bimini Road is a natural formation.

    B. The Bimini Road is man-made.

    C. The Bimini Road is evidence of the Thera eruption.

    D. The Bimini Road is evidence of an ancient earthquake.

5. As used in the passage, the word *enigma* most nearly means

    A. story.

    B. mystery.

    C. place.

    D. island.

6. Which of the following best states the author's feelings about of the existence of Atlantis?

    A. The author wavers back and forth about the existence of Atlantis.

    B. The author does not reveal his or her opinion.

    C. The author believes Atlantis is not fictional.

    D. The author believes Atlantis is fictional.

DIRECTIONS: *Read the passage and answer the questions that follow it.*

Ada Byron

AUGUSTA ADA BYRON was the only legitimate daughter of the poet Lord George Gordon Byron. Lord Byron and Annabella Milbanke Noel were married in 1815, but quickly divorced after Augusta's birth, December 10, 1815. Noel suspected Byron of having an affair with her sister. She also could not tolerate his mood swings. Noel was granted sole custody of Ada and provided Ada with home tutors who raised her to be a mathematician and scientist. Although her mother discouraged Ada from poetic interests, several

of Ada's letters demonstrate she had interests similar her father's. In a letter later written to her mother, she stated, "If you can't give me poetry, can't you give me 'poetical science'?"

As a teenager, Ada was introduced to a **prominent** female mathematician, Mary Somerville. While attending one of Somerville's parties, she learned of Charles Babbage's ideas for what he called the Analytical Engine. Ada quickly understood his theories and began working with him on the world's first computer. Upon discovering the machine could calculate Bernoulli numbers, she created the first computer program. She also predicted the machine would later be able to design graphics and compose music. Over the years, she translated many of Babbage's papers and added her own notes, which were often longer than his original papers. However, they remained mostly unexamined by future computer engineers. In 1979, a software language developed by the U.S. Department of Defense was named "ADA" in her honor.

During her work with Babbage, Ada married the future Lord Lovelace, William King, at the age of nineteen. After the birth of their third child, she suffered from a physical, mental, and emotional breakdown. Doctors prescribed her combinations of drugs and alcohol that would be considered **lethal** today. While under the medications, Ada experienced visions and believed she could understand the mind of God. After losing her battle to cancer, Ada died at the age of thirty-six. Per her request, she was buried beside her father, whom she never knew, in the Byron family vault. **⊙**

QUESTIONS

1. Which of the following best states the purpose of this passage?

    A. to inform the reader about the Lady of Lovelace's family life

    B. to explain how a woman contributed to the first computer

    C. to describe how far computer technology has come

    D. to inform the reader about a famous royal figure

2. What led to Ada's aptitude with math and science?

    A. Ada's mother was a mathematician.

    B. Ada rebelled against her mother and furthered her own interests.

    C. Ada's mother did not want Ada to be like her father.

    D. Ada demonstrated natural tendencies toward math and science.

3. Which of the following best states the reason for the first paragraph?

    A. It explains the marital strife of Ada's parents.

    B. It describes Ada's early life.

    C. It was written to dishonor the memory of the Romantic poet, Lord Byron.

    D. It explains how Ada became like her father despite her mother's wishes.

4. According to the passage, which statement is true?

    A. Lord Byron had fathered other children.

    B. Noel was able to rid Ada of all poetic interests.

    C. Ada and Charles Babbage were in love.

    D. Ada's scientific work is of no significance today.

5. As used in the passage, the word *lethal* most nearly means

    A. practical.

    B. illegal.

    C. harmless.

    D. deadly.

6. *Answer the following question using complete sentences:*

    What might Ada have meant by her desire for "poetical science"?

DIRECTIONS: *Read the passage and answer the questions that follow it.*

Gloria Steinem

GLORIA STEINEM (1934 – present) is a feminist writer, editor, and speaker. Since the launch of the women's liberation movement in the1960s, she has been politically active in the pursuit of equality and social reformation. Steinem began her career as a **freelance** journalist after graduating from Smith College in 1956, and studying at universities in Delhi and Calcutta, India. Her influential articles quickly called attention to the need for social and cultural change. For a more stable writing career, she worked at a New

York magazine where her major breakthrough came from an article she wrote that exposed the treatment of women in the entertainment industry. In 1972, Steinem co-founded and became the editor of *Ms. Magazine*, which gave her the platform to discuss various social issues including reproductive rights, discrimination in the workplace, and stereotyping based on gender roles. The publication enjoyed a wide readership for fifteen years until conflict with advertisers resulted in the magazine's demise. In 1990, the magazine was reborn and featured an article discussing the control advertisers have on the content of women's magazines and the effects on readers.

Although she is famous for her literary works as a feminist, she has also played an active role in civil rights issues, peace campaigns, and politics. As a popular speaker, she often addresses audiences several times a week and demonstrates that feminism is an issue for all women, regardless of their ethnicity or socioeconomic status. In 1971, Steinem and a group of other **predominant** feminists founded the National Women's Political Caucus, an organization designed to encourage women to run for political office. She is a co-founder and president of the board of directors for the Ms. Foundation for Women and a founding member of the Coalition of Labor Union Women.

Although some have criticized her work and opinions, she remains an influential leader and public figure. Her various social commentaries continue to be popular and serve to improve the status of women. Her work will continue to improve the status of women for years to come. ●

QUESTIONS

1. Which of the following best states the author's purpose?
- **A.** to describe the women's liberation movement
- **B.** to explain why Gloria Steinem should be president
- **C.** to describe the role of an influential feminist
- **D.** to explain Steinem's political achievements

2. Which of the following would be the best title for this passage?
- **A.** Feminist Issues
- **B.** Steinem's Fight for Freedom
- **C.** Feminism in Today's Society
- **D.** Fighting for Favoritism

3. Which of the following issues would Steinem probably not endorse?
- **A.** campaigning for a female president
- **B.** mandating equal pay for men and women who perform the same job
- **C.** creating more female athletic teams
- **D.** producing films that include chauvinistic humor

4. According to the passage, which statement is true?
- **A.** Steinem has held a political office.
- **B.** Steinem began her writing career while attending college.
- **C.** Steinem has played a small role in the fight for feminism.
- **D.** Steinem believes advertising can impact women.

5. Which best describes the reason for the first paragraph?
- **A.** It exposes Steinem's contempt for the magazine industry.
- **B.** It highlights her work as an author.
- **C.** It urges the reader to buy Ms. *magazine.*
- **D.** It describes some of Steinem's feminist views.

6. As used in the passage, the word *predominant* most nearly means
- **A.** important.
- **B.** trivial.
- **C.** inconspicuous.
- **D.** accepted.

DIRECTIONS: *Read the passage and answer the questions that follow it.*

School Violence

On the morning of April 20, 1999, at Columbine High School in Littleton, Colorado, twelve students and one teacher perished and twenty-four others were wounded. The massacre ended once the assailants, Eric Harris and Dylan Klebold, took their own lives. This shocking school shooting was featured on news broadcasts around the country for days. How could such a tragedy happen in a quiet suburban school? But the horrific episode was not an **isolated** incident—at least a dozen others happened during an eighteen-month period.

Some people have criticized the media attention given to school shootings, claiming that it only inspires other students to perform "copy cat" crimes in America and Canada. Others responded to the Columbine massacre by debating gun control and raising concerns about easy access to firearms. Still, more began to point fingers at violent music, films, and video games. With widespread concern about the causes of violence, various government investigations were launched to analyze the reasons for school shootings and find ways these incidents could be prevented. After investigating eighteen school shootings in depth, the FBI's National Center for the Analysis of Violent Crime (NCAVC) released a report titled "The School Shooter: A Threat Assessment Perspective" to present a model procedure for threat assessment and **intervention**.

The report states that overall, school violence is falling, not rising. It is the shock and fear that follows a violent incident that makes the public concerned about violence. Violence, anywhere, is complex, and there are no easy answers. However, violent behavior develops progressively with observable signs as a person progresses to advanced stages. Acknowledging the potential for violence, the report urges faculty to take all threats seriously. A threat is defined as an expression of intent to do harm or act out violently; it can be spoken, written, or symbolic. One Secret Service report notes that in more than seventy-five percent of school shootings, at least one student knew of the potential violence but did not report it. Government agencies are stressing to faculties the importance of getting students to speak up. If you know of a potential threat, tell a teacher, guidance counselor, or administrator. It could save lives. ◗

QUESTIONS

1. Why did the author write this passage?
   A. to inform the reader about the increase in school shootings
   B. to describe the massacre at Columbine High School
   C. to describe a school shooting and the response to the media's coverage
   D. to explain why school shootings happen in suburban schools

2. Which of the following would be the best title for this passage?
   A. Columbine Killings
   B. Can School Violence Be Stopped?
   C. The FBI and the Secret Service Invade Our Schools
   D. The Increase of School Violence

3. Which of the following best states the reason for the second paragraph?
   A. It proves that violence in our culture is causing violence in schools.
   B. It explains how the media can cause "copy cat" crimes.
   C. It describes the role of the NCAVC.
   D. It addresses various ways people responded to school shootings.

4. According to the passage, which of the following statements is true?
   A. School violence is increasing in America.
   B. Threats should not be taken seriously because most are never carried out.
   C. Eric Harris and Dylan Klebold are responsible for the deaths at Columbine.
   D. Violence is always perpetrated by male students.

5. As used in the passage, the word *intervention* most nearly means
   A. prevention.
   B. antagonism.
   C. indifference.
   D. aggravation.

6. *Answer the following question using complete sentences:*
   Why might students be reluctant to report a threat?

DIRECTIONS: *Read the passage and answer the questions that follow it.*

The Transcontinental Railroad

THE U.S. **TRANSCONTINENTAL** RAILROAD, which stretches from the eastern states to California, was built during the 1860s. Previously, the eastern portion of the railway, called the Union Pacific Railroad, extended from Nebraska to Iowa. The western portion, or the Central Pacific Railroad, began in Sacramento, California. To join the two systems, laborers worked on both railways, laying track until the two systems met. Men who worked on the railroad earned between one and three dollars a day while working twelve hours per day, six days a week, in all types of weather. For tools, the men used wheelbarrows, rope, blasting powder, axes, and mules. Most of the laborers on the Union Pacific track were Irish, Mormons, and veterans from the Union and Confederate armies. The group averaged approximately a mile of track a day across the plains. Their main difficulties involved securing funding and interacting with Native Americans, who were angry about the whites' encroachment on their lands. The workforce on the Central Pacific railway were mostly Chinese, who were hired to fill the white labor shortage. Amid enduring racism, these laborers also suffered through inclement weather and had to break through ground of solid rock without the most effective tools.

By the time the track was finished on May 10, 1869, at the Golden Spike event in Utah, at Promontory Summit, western laborers had laid 690 miles of track while eastern workers had laid 1,087. Although the Transcontinental Railroad was ultimately a success, many financial difficulties, legislative issues, and ethical dilemmas arose throughout its construction. For example, Northerners and Southerners wanted their own routes, but initially, Congress was undecided about whether slavery should be permitted in the "New West"; consequently, the debate about the exact route and the connecting location remained unsettled. For the most part, the track-building companies determined the routes, but were unable to decide upon a meeting place. As the Civil War raged, the situation, and people's opinions, changed. Since the railroad was intended to unify the country, the government finally assigned Promontory Summit as the location to wed the rails. Ultimately, the **arduous** labor and numerous impasses proved worthwhile, as the new railroad indeed united America. ○

QUESTIONS

1. Which of the following best states the author's purpose?
- **A.** to inform the reader about the different racial groups that labored on the railroad
- **B.** to explain how the Transcontinental Railroad was built
- **C.** to describe the legislative controversies surrounding the construction of the railroad
- **D.** to describe the effects of the railroad on Native Americans

2. Which of the following would be the best title for this passage?
- **A.** Railroad Diaries
- **B.** Riding the Rails
- **C.** Uniting the Country
- **D.** Laying Iron Rails

3. What was the purpose of the Transcontinental Railroad?
- **A.** to enable recreational travel
- **B.** to create American jobs
- **C.** to facilitate commuting
- **D.** to unite the country

4. As used in the passage, the word *arduous* most nearly means
- **A.** backbreaking.
- **B.** violent.
- **C.** motivating.
- **D.** effortless.

5. According to the passage, which of the following statements is true?
- **A.** The Transcontinental Railroad allowed for slave transportation into the New West.
- **B.** Laborers used advanced tools and technologies to build the new railway system.
- **C.** Completion of the railroad required several decades.
- **D.** The railroad impeded upon Native American territory.

6. *Answer the following question using complete sentences:*
Why did many people oppose the use of a Chinese labor force?

DIRECTIONS: *Read the passage and answer the questions that follow it.*

Sam Patch

SAM PATCH (1799–1829) was approximately seven years old when he began working as a child laborer in a mill in Pawtucket, Rhode Island. He was a successful mule spinner, or one who created cotton threads for **textiles**. During his mid twenties, he relocated and worked at a mill in Paterson, New Jersey, where he began jumping off the mill dam to entertain fellow employees. As he began jumping from greater heights, audiences gathered to observe his feats. One of his first major jumps was from a height of seventy feet at Passaic Falls, New Jersey. He continued his career by leaping from bridges, factory walls, and masts of ships. Although doing so is illegal today, he became the fist person to jump Niagara Falls successfully, in an event designed to increase tourism to the falls. During his second attempt, 10,000 people gathered to watch him. Often, Patch would advertise his performances and attracted journalists who featured him in articles. Known as the Yankee Leaper, Patch started fusing a political agenda into his jumps, using them as opportunities to expose issues of the working class.

rpf00190.jpg Rochester Public Library Local History Division

On November 13, 1829, Patch planned to jump the Upper Falls at Niagara. After a pre-jump celebration, he dove into the water inebriated and was unable to land a feet-first, vertical entry. When he did not resurface, some speculated he was hiding in a cave. The rumors were **dispelled** when his frozen body was found months later by Silas Hudson. It was determined his shoulders were dislocated on impact, and he drowned. His bravery is remembered through the works of famous authors such as Hawthorne, Poe, and Melville. Additionally, he is frequently mentioned in comic strips and plays. Over the thirty-year-old man's grave is placed wooden board bearing the following inscription: "Sam Patch—Such is Fame." ◗

QUESTIONS

1. Which of the following best states the author's purpose?
 A. to describe the career of an early daredevil
 B. to explain how drinking alcohol can impair judgment
 C. to describe the dangers of leaping from incredible heights
 D. to explain how fame can be used for political influence

2. Which of the following would be the best title for this passage?
 A. Leaping Lunatics
 B. Jumping for Congress
 C. Dangerous Daredevils
 D. Niagara's Famous Jumper

3. What is the purpose of the first paragraph?
 A. It defines the duties of a mule spinner.
 B. It explains how Sam Patch got his nickname.
 C. It describes Sam Patch's role as a political activist.
 D. It explains how Sam Patch became famous.

4. According to the passage, which statement is true?
 A. Patch jumped from government buildings during times of protest.
 B. He generally drew small audiences to his jumps.
 C. Patch was the first successful jumper of Niagara Falls.
 D. Child labor was illegal during the nineteenth century.

5. As used in the passage, the word *dispelled* most nearly means
 A. proven.
 B. rejected.
 C. disproved.
 D. created.

6. *Answer the following question using complete sentences:*
 What might be the meaning of the inscription above Sam Patch's grave?

DIRECTIONS: *Read the passage and answer the questions that follow it.*

Family and Medical Leave

ENACTED ON FEBRUARY 5, 1993, the Family and Medical Leave Act was one of President Bill Clinton's first major bills. It was created to allow employees to take unpaid leave to deal with a variety of family and medical issues. The Act was drafted by the National Partnership for Women and Families, a **nonprofit** organization that promotes fairness in the workplace and quality health care. The law recognizes peoples' needs for balance between work and family. The protections allow a worker up to twelve weeks orfleave annually for reasons such as caring for newborns, adoption or foster care placement, caring for sick relatives, or personal illness. The worker is guaranteed his or her job upon return or one equal in pay, benefits, and responsibility. The employee's benefits are also protected during leave. It is important to note that the Act applies only to those employed at companies with more than fifty employees within a seventy-five mile radius. The employee must have been employed by the company for at least twelve months and worked more than 1,250 hours. All U.S. government employees and state employees are protected under the Act.

The Act has been criticized as making **provisions** that are more often used by female employees. Since female employees might then be considered more expensive than males, subtle discrimination practices will likely occur during the hiring process. Supporters encourage critics to view the Act as beneficial to both genders, allowing all employees to take care of family members without being penalized in the workplace. Men have the same rights as women under the Act; if they utilize those rights as often as women, discrimination practices will not occur. ●

QUESTIONS

1. What is the author's purpose?
   A. to describe a piece of legislation that is under attack by anti-feminists
   B. to explain how workers can take leave from jobs and be protected
   C. to describe a piece of legislation that protects employers from employees who take excessive leave
   D. to show how the government protects federal employees

2. Which of the following would be the best title for this passage?
   A. Leaving Work
   B. How to Leave Work
   C. Clinton's Most Important Bill
   D. Balancing Family and Work

3. Which of the following best states the reason for the final paragraph?
   A. It describes how the Act will contribute to more discrimination at work.
   B. It explains why women are not hired as often as men.
   C. It informs the reader about opposing views of the Act.
   D. It shows how men and women can benefit from the Act.

4. Which incident would probably not be protected under the Act?
   A. leave for the hospitalization of a spouse
   B. leave for a family vacation
   C. leave for the adoption of a child
   D. leave for aiding a sick parent

5. According to the passage, which statement is true?
   A. The Act allows workers to receive regular pay while taking leave.
   B. The Act was created to help both genders balance family issues.
   C. The Act guarantees leave to all U.S. workers.
   D. The Act was drafted by President Bill Clinton.

6. As used in the passage, the word *provisions* most nearly means
   A. conditions.
   B. qualifications.
   C. limitations.
   D. customs.

DIRECTIONS: *Read the passage and answer the questions that follow it.*

Robert LeRoy Ripley

BORN ON DECEMBER 25, 1890, in Santa Rosa, California, Robert LeRoy Ripley was a self-taught artist and a remarkable athlete. At the age of fourteen, he sold his first cartoon to *LIFE* magazine and got a job with the *San Francisco Bulletin* the following year. After moving to New York in 1912, he created a sports cartoon, called "Champs and Chumps," for the *New York Globe*, and began traveling worldwide to cover events. He had hoped to become a professional baseball player but was injured during his first game in 1913. While working on "Champs and Chumps," Ripley changed the title to *Believe It or Not!* and used the cartoon as a **forum** to expose oddities from around the globe. During its peak, the cartoon had a readership of 80 million, making him one of the most famous people in the world.

After having journeyed to the most remote areas in 201 countries to collect information for his series, he was called the "modern Marco Polo." Of all the places Ripley visited, China was his favorite. "If I could be reincarnated, I'd return as a Chinese [person]," he stated. In 1949, Ripley began to televise his real-life oddities, which featured cultural practices, customs, and beliefs of ancient and modern civilizations. During the thirteenth episode, Ripley collapsed. Airing of his original series ceased, and his health continued to fail. He died on May 27, 1949, of a heart attack. Although he has passed, his legacy lives on in television and radio programs, various publications, and twenty-seven museums worldwide. Some have accused Ripley of **exaggerating** his reports, but Ripley always claimed to be able to prove every statement he ever made. ●

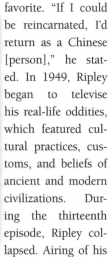

QUESTIONS

1. Why did the author write this passage?

    A. to explain the popularity of *Ripley's Believe It or Not!*

    B. to describe the creator of *Ripley's Believe It or Not!*

    C. to inform the reader about a famous cartoonist

    D. to compare Ripley to famous explorers

2. What is the purpose of the first paragraph?

    A. It describes how Ripley combined his passions to become famous.

    B. It explains how Ripley started his cartoon.

    C. It describes Ripley's early life in California.

    D. It explains why Ripley never became a professional athlete.

3. As used in the passage, the word *forum* most nearly means

    A. facility.

    B. stunt.

    C. marketplace.

    D. medium.

4. According to the passage, which statement is true?

    A. Ripley sold his first cartoon to the *San Francisco Bulletin*.

    B. Ripley often exaggerated his findings to make his material more interesting.

    C. Ripley was a successful artist from a young age.

    D. Ripley died while taping the thirteenth episode of his television show.

5. According to the passage, which group of words correctly identifies Ripley?

    A. celebrity, professional athlete, artist

    B. cartoonist, adventurer, reporter

    C. athlete, reporter, father

    D. artist, publicist, actor

6. Which of the following would be the best title for this passage?

    A. Ripley's Champs and Chumps

    B. Ripley's American Adventures

    C. Remember Ripley

    D. The Oddities of Ripley

DIRECTIONS: *Read the passage and answer the questions that follow it.*

PETA

People for the **Ethical** Treatment of Animals (PETA), founded in 1980, is the world's largest nonprofit animal rights organization with more than one million members and supporters worldwide. Outside the headquarters in Norfolk, Virginia, several international offices are affiliated with PETA's focus on animals used in factory farms, vivisection (animal testing), the clothing trade, and entertainment. The group spreads its message and draws attention to its causes through various means, including public education campaigns, animal cruelty investigations, scientific research, animal rescue efforts, and protest demonstrations.

PETA first gained public attention in 1981, after becoming involved in a case in Silver Spring, Maryland. During the investigation of a primate laboratory, several documented cases of abuse and neglect were found, which resulted in the first conviction of an animal experimenter on charges of cruelty to animals. Since then, the organization has promoted many successful campaigns exposing companies' lack of ethics and boycotting large corporations, such as Kentucky Fried Chicken, Procter and Gamble, and PETCO, thus improving the well being and treatment of countless animals.

The organization has used drastic methods to promote its ideals. Alex Pacheco, a PETA founder, stated "arson, property destruction, burglary, and theft are acceptable crimes when used for the animal cause." To promote vegetarianism, PETA has utilized religious themes, made comparisons of slaughtered animals to the Holocaust, and displayed **scantily** clad women (called "Lettuce Ladies") in public to distribute information. Popular celebrities and activists have appeared in various PETA awareness campaigns. Although many of PETA's campaigns have drawn national attention, it is perhaps their controversial methods that generate the greatest response. Many groups and individuals are displeased with PETA's offensive campaigns. Opponents have accused PETA of misleading members, euthanizing the animals they liberate, funding terrorist organizations, and putting animal rights over human welfare. ●

QUESTIONS

1. Why did the author write this passage?
- **A.** to inform the reader about companies who abuse animals
- **B.** to explain the controversial actions of PETA members
- **C.** to promote an animal-free lifestyle
- **D.** to inform the reader about an animal rights group

2. Which of the following would be the best title for this passage?
- **A.** PETA: People Eating Tasty Animals
- **B.** Stopping Animal Abuse
- **C.** Fighting for Animal Rights
- **D.** Coexisting With Cuddly Creatures

3. Which of the following is not one of PETA's major concerns?
- **A.** factory farms
- **B.** clothing trade
- **C.** entertainment animals
- **D.** vegetarian support

4. As used in the passage, *scantily* most nearly means
- **A.** professionally.
- **B.** inadequately.
- **C.** specially.
- **D.** distastefully.

5. Which best describes the reason for the final paragraph?
- **A.** It exposes the author's personal opinion about PETA.
- **B.** It describes some alternative views about the organization.
- **C.** It exposes some successful PETA campaigns.
- **D.** It portrays Pacheco as a radical.

6. According to the passage, which statement is true?
- **A.** PETA believes animals should be treated with the same respect as humans.
- **B.** PETA is a for-profit organization.
- **C.** PETA has not been successful in changing legislation regarding animal cruelty.
- **D.** PETA members have all committed crimes to save animals.

DIRECTIONS: *Read the passage and answer the questions that follow it.*

The Guillotine

THE **GUILLOTINE** WAS A DEVICE designed to execute by means of decapitation. A blade, suspended at the top of a tall frame, would be dropped to sever the victim's head. Although it became famous during the French Revolution (1789-1799), earlier guillotine-like devices were used before the 1300s throughout Germany, Great Britain, and Italy. One of the earliest decapitating machines was England's Halifax Gibbet, a fifteen-foot high wooden structure featuring an axe head attached to a wooden block. Executions were held in the town's marketplace on Saturdays dating from the 1280s until 1650. While most guillotine executions were reserved for the wealthy in most countries, the Halifax Gibbet was used for all classes who broke the law. Another device was the Scottish Maiden, whose first documented use was to execute Murcod Ballagh in Ireland in 1307. Its design was very similar to the later French guillotine.

Throughout early eighteenth century France, many gruesome methods were employed to punish common criminals and deter others from committing the same crimes. Some examples include drawing-and-quartering and burning people at the stake, both of which were especially barbaric and painful. The nobility were punished by decapitation, which theoretically would be quick and relatively painless; however, the axes were often too light or dull to sever the head in a single blow, making repeated attempts necessary. Many prominent members of society began questioning these **atrocious** methods, including Dr. Joseph-Ignace Guillotin. With a sketch of a guillotine, he proposed six articles to the Legislative Assembly beginning in 1789, in hopes of reformation. In Article 2, he wrote:

> In all cases where the law imposes the death penalty on an accused person, the punishment shall be the same, whatever the nature of the offence of which he is guilty; the criminal shall be decapitated; this will be done solely by means of a simple mechanism.

In 1791, when the Legislative Assembly decreed, "every person condemned to the death penalty shall have his head severed," France became the first country to make the guillotine the standard method of execution for all classes. ●

QUESTIONS

1. What is the author's purpose?
- **A.** to inform the reader about primitive methods of capital punishment
- **B.** to describe the use of decapitating machines through the French Revolution
- **C.** to prove the French were not the fist to use decapitating machines
- **D.** to explain why the guillotine was used in England

2. Which of the following best describes French death penalty methods prior to the French Revolution?
- **A.** They were especially brutal.
- **B.** They were used for the peasant class.
- **C.** They were always used for the upper class.
- **D.** They were a forbidden practice.

3. Which of the following best states the reason for the first paragraph?
- **A.** It describes earlier methods of capital punishment.
- **B.** It informs the reader about guillotine-like devices.
- **C.** It explains why decapitating machines were used.
- **D.** It defines the guillotine.

4. According to the passage, which statement is true?
- **A.** Beheadings were a common method of capital punishment for all classes in France throughout the early eighteenth century.
- **B.** Decapitating machines were first used in France.
- **C.** The guillotine was used as a more humane method of execution.
- **D.** The design of the Halifax Gibbet closely resembled the later French guillotine.

5. Which best describes Dr. Guillotin's interest in the decapitation machine?
- **A.** He invented the machine to make cleanup easier after executions.
- **B.** He proposed using the machine as a way to reform capital punishment.
- **C.** He invented the machine to make a profit.
- **D.** He proposed using the machine to make the deaths of nobles more painless.

6. As used in the passage, the word *atrocious* most nearly means
- **A.** horrid.
- **B.** inoffensive.
- **C.** ancient.
- **D.** powerful.

DIRECTIONS: *Read the passage and answer the questions that follow it.*

NASCAR

THE DAYTONA 500 WAS THE FIRST NAS-CAR stock car race to be nationally televised, airing in 1979 on CBS. In the final lap, leaders Cale Yarborough and Donnie Allison crashed, and Richard Petty won. Afterwards, Yarborough and Allison engaged in a fistfight. This was the beginning of the drama race fans yearn for today.

NASCAR has undergone several stages of evolution since its inception. Earlier drivers were involved in bootlegging (a term for those involved with the illegal production and/or distribution of liquor) and modified their street vehicles to make them more evasive from police. Once they had made their vehicles faster and more **maneuverable**, they decided to race them. When these early races gained popularity throughout the rural South, William France, Sr., and Ed Otto promoted races before WWII. The men realized that the racing needed to be sanctioned; thus they founded the NASCAR organization in 1948. Approved racecars were strictly stock and had virtually no modifications. By the mid-1960s, however, cars were modified to allow for safety and performance yet still appeared fresh from the factory. Before speedways were designed with wider, high-banked sides, races were held on one-half to one-mile oval tracks.

Currently, NASCAR races are held on tracks of varying lengths and shapes, and the vehicles are anything but the stock cars used in the past. The organization also oversees seven regional series and more than 1,500 races on over 100 tracks throughout the U.S., Canada, and Mexico. The courses, each with different banks and curves, contribute to different possible top speeds. Talladega Superspeedway is the fastest track, with a record speed of 188 miles per hour. Racecars feature specially designed suspensions, breaks, and **aerodynamic** components. Unrestricted vehicles produce over 800 horsepower and can achieve speeds in excess of 200 miles per hour. According to regulations, only vehicles manufactured in the U.S. are permitted to race on NASCAR tracks.

Today, NASCAR is the second most popular sport watched on television in the U.S., losing first place to the National Football League. Internationally, races are broadcast in more than 150 countries. From 1996-1998, NASCAR even held exhibition races in Japan. From small beginnings, this captivating sport continues to grow in popularity around the world. ○

QUESTIONS

1. What is the author's purpose in writing this passage?

    A. to show how popular NASCAR racing has become

    B. to explain why fans are passionate about NASCAR

    C. to describe the careers of William France, Sr., and Ed Otto

    D. to explain how NASCAR evolved into the sport it is today

2. What can be inferred from the fact that NASCAR held exhibition races in Japan?

    A. NASCAR wants to use Japanese cars.

    B. NASCAR plans to sell stock in Japan.

    C. NASCAR is looking for new tracks.

    D. NASCAR is popular worldwide.

3. Which best describes the reason for the first paragraph?

    A. It describes the career of Cale Yarborough.

    B. It shows why some fans are interested in NASCAR.

    C. It makes the reader more interested in the passage.

    D. It demonstrates how dangerous the sport can be.

4. According to the passage, which statement is true?

    A. NASCAR was associated with illegal activities in previous years.

    B. The Daytona Superspeedway is the fastest NASCAR track.

    C. Any modified vehicle can be raced on a NASCAR track.

    D. NASCAR is more popular than football.

5. According to the passage, which statement is false?

    A. The first NASCAR race was televised on CBS.

    B. Unrestricted vehicles can travel at speeds over 180 mph.

    C. NASCAR races are only televised in the U.S.

    D. NASCAR began as a rural sport in the South.

6. *Answer the following question using complete sentences:*
What are the dangers of being a NASCAR driver?

DIRECTIONS: *Read the passage and answer the questions that follow it.*

Narcolepsy

NARCOLEPSY IS A **CHRONIC** DISEASE of the central nervous system. The first symptom, excessive daytime sleepiness (EDS), is present in all patients. Other symptoms include uncontrollable sleep attacks, hallucinations, sleep paralysis, and cataplexy, or the sudden loss of muscle tone. Patients often experience disturbances during **nocturnal** sleep. Narcoleptics compare the sleepiness they experience to the feeling of trying to stay awake after not sleeping for a few days. During a sleep attack, a narcoleptic suddenly falls asleep anywhere at any time for a period of a few seconds to over an hour. These attacks can be embarrassing, inconvenient, and even dangerous depending on where and when they occur. Some narcoleptics continue their activity while sleeping yet have no memory of the event once they awake. When patients experience a sleep attack, they immediately enter REM (rapid eye movement) sleep, the stage one enters while dreaming. During normal sleep, people typically enter a period of REM after approximately ninety minutes.

Narcolepsy usually has its onset during the teenage years as EDS, and narcolepsy often goes unrecognized until more frequent and severe symptoms develop over time. While the incidence of narcolepsy varies by country, it affects approximately 125,000 to 200,000 Americans. However, only approximately 50,000 are properly diagnosed. In 1999, scientists identified a narcolepsy gene that is responsible for some cases. The mutated gene allows cells in the hypothalamus to receive messages from other cells, which causes improper communication and abnormal sleeping patterns. Although it sometimes runs in families, only between eight to twelve percent of patients know of a relative with the disorder. Diagnosis can be made instantly if the patient has a history of EDS and cataplexy. Laboratory tests, such as those that monitor brain waves or the onset of REM sleep, can be completed to confirm narcolepsy. A genetic blood test can also be performed to check for narcolepsy, but its conclusions do not prove the existence of the disorder. Although narcolepsy is not a fatal disorder, it is chronic. And although there is no cure, patients can manage symptoms with lifestyle adjustments and medication. **O**

QUESTIONS

1. Why did the author write this passage?

    A. to inform the reader about popular sleep disorders

    B. to describe a neurological disease

    C. to explain the symptoms of narcolepsy

    D. to inform the reader about regular sleep patterns

2. Which on of the following symptoms is present in all narcolepsy patients?

    A. sleep attacks

    B. hallucinations

    C. daytime sleepiness

    D. cataplexy

3. According to the passage, which of the following statements is true?

    A. During cataplexy, muscles become tight and remain flexed.

    B. Narcolepsy is a hereditary disorder.

    C. Diagnosis can only be made through laboratory tests.

    D. Narcolepsy is a lifelong disease.

4. Which statement can be inferred from the information provided in the passage?

    A. The disease can interfere with a patient's daily life.

    B. Narcolepsy is easily and effectively diagnosed in most patients.

    C. The hypothalamus does not contribute to sleep regulation.

    D. Sleep attacks are only inconvenient if they occur while driving.

5. As used in the passage, the word *nocturnal* most nearly means

    A. evening.

    B. morning.

    C. heavy.

    D. light.

6. Which of the following methods would not help a narcoleptic manage symptoms?

    A. attempting to get a solid eight hours of sleep

    B. taking frequent, short naps during the day

    C. exercising in the morning or afternoon

    D. increasing caffeine consumption

DIRECTIONS: *Read the passage and answer the questions that follow it.*

Mount Everest

Known in Nepal as *Sagarmatha*, the "Forehead of the Sky," and in Tibet as *Chomolungma*, "Mother of the Universe," Mount Everest is the highest mountain on Earth. Its summit, which reaches approximately 29,017 feet above sea level, borders Nepal and China. Every year, the mountain grows 2.5 centimeters. The English name was given by Sir Andrew Waugh, a British surveyor-general of India. He chose to name the mountain after his **predecessor**, Sir George Everest. In 1852, Radhanath Sikdar, and Indian mathematician, was the first to use trigonometry to identify the mountain as having the highest peak. Since these calculations were performed, several teams have taken new measurements over the years. Other mountains have boasted the claim "highest mountain on earth" when measurements are taken from different locations. For example, Mauna Kea in Hawaii is the highest, over 5.6 miles, when measured from its base. Chimborazo in Ecuador is farthest from the Earth's center at 3,967.1 miles. However, both of these mountains fail to measure up to Everest when measured from sea level.

Many expeditions have attempted to summit Mount Everest since 1921. There are two main climbing routes for those to dare to attempt to reach the top: the southeast ridge, from Nepal, and the northeast ridge, from Tibet. The southeast route has been trekked more frequently since it is easier to scale; moreover, the Tibetan route was formerly closed to foreigners. Most attempts are made during April and May because climbing conditions are optimal: wind speeds are lower, and it is not yet monsoon season, which occurs in the summer. If climbers wait until September, additional snow makes climbing more difficult. Depending on the course of ascent, climbers are faced with different route challenges and difficulties **acclimating** to the conditions of higher altitudes while trying to reach the summit. Once climbers reach the death zone at 26,000 feet, oxygen tanks are necessary for continuation. Climbers are also faced with severe weather and altitude sickness, which is the result of the body's inability to adjust to such low air pressure and oxygen levels. Despite all this, many successful expeditions have made it to the summit, but it is perhaps the unfortunate experiences and disasters that have received the most publicity. ●

QUESTIONS

1. **Which of the following best states the author's purpose?**
    A. to inform the reader about historical climbs on Mount Everest
    B. to describe the history of Mount Everest
    C. to describe Mount Everest and its popularity with climbers
    D. to inform the reader about the challenges of climbing Mount Everest

2. **Which of the following would be the best title for this passage?**
    A. Scaling the Summit
    B. Quest for Everest
    C. Mountain Dangers
    D. Trekking the Highest Mountain

3. **Which of the following best states the reason for the final paragraph?**
    A. It describes the difficulties of climbing Everest.
    B. It informs the reader about the media's role in making Everest famous.
    C. It describes the difference between the northeast and southeast ridge.
    D. It provides details about the best time to attempt the summit.

4. **As used in the passage, the word *acclimating* most nearly means**
    A. adjusting.
    B. ignoring.
    C. absorbing.
    D. continuing.

5. **Which best describes the reason for the first paragraph?**
    A. It describes the origin of the mountain's name.
    B. It informs the reader about Everest's growth.
    C. It names important discoverers who contributed to Everest's fame.
    D. It proves that Everest really is the highest mountain on Earth.

6. *Answer the following question using complete sentences:*
    Why might disasters on the mountain receive more publicity than achievements?

DIRECTIONS: *Read the passage and answer the questions that follow it.*

Leprosy

LEPROSY, ALSO CALLED Hansen's disease, is a chronic, **infectious** disease that can cause a variety of deformities and disfigurements if left untreated. A Norwegian physician, named Gerhard Armauer Hansen, discovered a rod-shaped, fast acting bacterium, called *Mycobacterium leprae* in 1874. Although the mode of transmission is not definite, the disease is believed to be passed through mucus and skin sores. It may also be transmitted through contact with contaminated objects and arthropods, including insects, spiders, and crustaceans. Approximately five percent of those exposed contract leprosy. Two forms of the disease exist, and both progress gradually, sometimes taking years for symptoms to appear. Although the disease is not fatal, it affects the skin, nerves, and mucous membranes. Many believe the disease to cause a rotting of the flesh, but this is a misconception. The disease causes inflammation and destruction of the skin; the body attempts to rid itself of the disease, causing overgrowths and deformities.

Diagnosis can be determined from samples taken from the sores or mucous membranes. Treatment depends on the severity and type of leprosy. Those with the lepromatous form usually live longer (than those with the tuberculoid form) despite the fact they often suffer more deformities. Combinations of drugs, including antibiotics, are used, usually for a lifetime, to control the disease. The World Health Organization is attempting to eradicate the disease completely; however, affordable drugs, early diagnosis, and affordable services are challenges.

Hansen's disease has existed since biblical times. The Old-Testament Book of Leviticus describes segregating patients and using disinfectants as a means to control the disease. Many skin diseases during this time were thought to be caused by leprosy. The disease was also found during 1350 B.C. in Egypt and was prevalent in India and Japan before 1000 B.C. The Crusades contributed to the spread of leprosy throughout Europe to the point of creating an epidemic during the thirteenth century. Historically, people were shunned and isolated in leper colonies. Some societies viewed the disease as a spiritual or human afflicted curse. During the Middle Ages, people believed the disease to be highly contagious and transmittable by a simple glance from a leper. Victims of the disease have historically been called lepers, a **pejorative** term that has been replaced with "people affected by leprosy."

Although it is often considered an ancient disease, leprosy occurs today in parts of Asia, Africa, and Latin America. It is especially prevalent in areas of overcrowding and poor sanitation. Cases have risen since the 1960s in the U.S. In areas such as California and the Northeast, where immigration is high, incidents of leprosy occur most often. ⦿

QUESTIONS

1. **What is the author's purpose?**
   - **A.** to inform the reader about the dangers of contracting leprosy
   - **B.** to explain an ancient disease that still exists today
   - **C.** to describe the symptoms of leprosy
   - **D.** to explain why lepers have been removed from society

2. **Which of the following would be the best title for this passage?**
   - **A.** The Dangers of Leprosy
   - **B.** Diagnosing Leprosy
   - **C.** Leprosy Today
   - **D.** Leprosy Yesterday and Today

3. **Which of the following best states the reason for the second paragraph?**
   - **A.** It informs the reader about the mission of the World Health Organization.
   - **B.** It describes the way lepers have been viewed historically.
   - **C.** It explains how leprosy can be diagnosed and treated.
   - **D.** It describes the difference between the lepromatous and tuberculoid forms.

4. **As used in the passage, the word *pejorative* most nearly means**
   - **A.** derogatory.
   - **B.** cruel.
   - **C.** insensitive.
   - **D.** inaccurate.

5. **According to the passage, which statement is false?**
   - **A.** Leprosy is a flesh eating disease.
   - **B.** The disease still affects global society today.
   - **C.** People believed lepers to be cursed by higher powers.
   - **D.** Leprosy is not a highly contagious disease.

6. **Which of the following best describes the purpose of the third paragraph?**
   - **A.** It explains why leper colonies existed.
   - **B.** It explains how the disease was spread to Europe.
   - **C.** It proves leprosy is the oldest documented disease.
   - **D.** It describes historical views of the disease.

DIRECTIONS: *Read the passage and answer the questions that follow it.*

Laser Hair Removal

As TECHNOLOGY EVOLVES and people become more frustrated with the daily hassles of shaving, the odor of **depilatory** creams, and the pain associated with waxing, laser hair removal is becoming increasingly popular. This technology promises to rid people of the regular inconvenience and agitation that are associated with typical hair-removal methods. In this procedure, laser energy is transferred to the hair follicle, which contains melanin, the agent responsible for giving hair and skin pigmentation. Melanin also surrounds the apparatus that causes hair growth.

When melanin absorbs laser energy, it is converted to heat, which causes damage to the follicle and stops future hair growth. Skin also contains melanin, but the laser energy is absorbed much faster in the hair follicle and takes longer to cool; therefore, more energy is absorbed into the follicle lying below the **epidermis** without damaging the surrounding skin.

Not all people are good candidates for laser hair removal because of the role melanin plays. For laser hair removal to be effective, a person's hair must be darker than the surrounding skin. It is almost impossible to remove blond, red, and gray hair from the body. Additionally, too much laser energy will be absorbed into the skin of a person with very dark pigmentation. However, those with dark skin or tanned patients with light hair can sometimes undergo laser hair removal at specialized centers.

While laser hair removal seems to be a permanent answer to the hair-hating problem, it is neither permanent nor is it absolute. Laser hair removal results in permanent *reduction*. Because of lawsuits and costly out-of-court settlements, many practices have gone out of business for promising permanent hair removal, and many others no longer guarantee results. Laser hair removal is neither cheap nor painless. Multiple sessions, five being the average, are required due to the fact that hair grows in cycles. Additionally, the laser is only capable of penetrating two millimeters into the skin, which is not deep enough to reach all roots. Each session costs hundreds of dollars depending on the extent of the area to be treated. Regardless, these facts do not keep men and women away from laser hair centers. ●

QUESTIONS

1. How does the laser remove hair?

   A. The heat damages the melanin.

   B. The heat damages the epidermis.

   C. The heat damages the follicle.

   D. The heat damages the hair.

2. Which of the following groups of words best describes laser hair removal?

   A. inexpensive, time consuming

   B. inexpensive, painful

   C. expensive, immediate

   D. expensive, prolonged

3. Which of the following best describes the reason for the second paragraph?

   A. It describes the best candidate for laser hair removal.

   B. It informs the reader about the risks associated with laser hair removal.

   C. It explains how the skin can become damaged by laser energy.

   D. It describes the importance of the hair follicle.

4. According to the passage, which statement is true?

   A. Laser hair removal permanently removes unwanted hair and prevents it from ever growing back.

   B. Laser hair removal can be difficult to afford because of high costs and repeated sessions.

   C. Laser energy is only absorbed by the melanin in the follicle and is not absorbed by the skin.

   D. Laser hair removal can be performed easily in one or two sessions.

5. As used in the passage, the word *epidermis* most nearly means

   A. skin.

   B. cells.

   C. hair.

   D. tissue.

6. *Answer the following question using complete sentences:*
What skin and hair color does the ideal candidate for laser hair removal have?

DIRECTIONS: *Read the passage and answer the questions that follow it.*

José Torres

JOSÉ TORRES WAS BORN on May 3, 1936, in Ponce, Puerto Rico. At the age of eighteen, Torres joined the U.S. Army, where he learned how to box. During the 1956 Olympic Games, Torres represented the U.S. in boxing and won a silver medal as a junior middleweight. He turned to professional boxing in 1958, and knocked-out George Hamilton during the first round in New York. After winning twelve consecutive fights—ten of which were knockouts—he fought in San Juan, Puerto Rico, against Benny Paret, who was a world welterweight and middleweight champion, to a ten-round draw.

Torres returned to Ponce in 1961, and fought Hamilton in a rematch **bout**, winning by a knockout. He won the following six fights that year, all by knockout. In 1963, his knockout streak ended in defeat to Florentino Fernandez of Argentina. Fernandez was the only professional fighter ever to beat Torres by knockout. After returning to training, Torres won by decision in a ten-round battle against Don Fullmer, a top contender, in New Jersey. After defeating several well-known boxers in 1964, Torres was ranked number one among light heavyweight challengers. In 1965, Torres became the third Puerto Rican world boxing champion in history and the first Latin American to win the light heavyweight title. He lost his title during his fourth bout in a fifteen-round fight against Dick Tiger, a hall-of-famer from Nigeria. During a rematch battle in 1967, Torres lost again, and a substantial riot **ensued** throughout New York City. Torres fought only twice after the defeat and retired in 1969.

After retiring, he became a representative of the Puerto Rican community in New York, meeting with politicians, giving lectures, and becoming New York State's athletic commissioner. In 1987, he published biographies about Mike Tyson and Muhammad Ali. From 1990 to 1995, he served as the president of the World Boxing Organization. The International Boxing Hall of Famer regularly contributes to a column for a Spanish newspaper in New York City. ⬤

QUESTIONS

1. Which if the following best states the author's purpose?

    A. to inform the reader about Hispanic boxers

    B. to describe the personal life of José Torres

    C. to explain how José Torres became a famous fighter

    D. to inform the reader about the sport of boxing

2. Which of the following would be the best title for this passage?

    A. José Torres: Olympic Gold Medallist

    B. José Torres: Army Boxer

    C. José Torres: Knockout Artist

    D. José Torres: American Boxer

3. As used in the passage, the word *ensued* most nearly means

    A. resulted.

    B. preceded.

    C. terminated.

    D. halted.

4. What is the purpose of the first paragraph?

    A. It describes the beginning of Torres' boxing career.

    B. It informs the reader about Torres' training.

    C. It explains how Torres was able to represent the U.S. as a citizen of Puerto Rico.

    D. It describes his accomplishments as an Olympian.

5. According to the passage, which statement is true?

    A. Torres won most of his fights by decision.

    B. Torres learned how to box while enlisted in the army.

    C. Torres began boxing professionally at the age of eighteen.

    D. Torres was the first Hispanic boxer to compete in the Olympic Games.

6. *Answer the following question using complete sentences:*
How did Torres use his fame after retirement?

DIRECTIONS: *Read the passage and answer the questions that follow it.*

The Atomic Bomb

THE END OF WORLD WAR II spread gradually from continent to continent. The final phase of the war involved the United States and Japan, which had been planning to invade and conquer the U.S. The threat of invasion and Japan's refusal to negotiate were so great that the U.S. determined it necessary to attack Japan and destroy the country's fighting abilities. On August 6, 1945, the United States Army forces dropped an atomic bomb on Hiroshima, and three days later, another on Nagasaki. The bombs were not dropped without purpose; the strategy was to influence Japan to surrender. The city of Hiroshima had been targeted because of its industrial and military operations. President Truman hoped that the bombings would bring a quick resolution to the war and spare future **casualties** for both sides. He made the following statement after the attack on Hiroshima:

"If they do not now accept our terms, they may expect a rain of ruin from the air the like of which has never been seen on this earth."

The "Little Boy" bomb dropped by the B-29 *Enola Gay* exploded 2,000 feet above the city. The blast, which was equivalent to thirteen kilotons of TNT, destroyed ninety percent of Hiroshima's buildings and killed more than 80,000 people instantaneously. By the end of the year, an additional 200,000 died from nuclear radiation. More than ninety percent of the victims were civilians. Those who survived the atomic bombings were called *hibakusha*, which literally means "bomb-affected people." The *hibakusha* were often victims of discrimination due to the misconceptions of radiation-related diseases. Japan surrendered on August 10, one day after the latter of the bombings, which were the first and only nuclear attacks in world history. Having experienced the devastation first-hand, Japan has since labored to **abolish** nuclear weapons around the world. ○

QUESTIONS

1. Why did the author write this passage?

    A. to inform the reader about the first atomic bomb used in war

    B. to explain how devastating nuclear bombs can be

    C. to explain why Japan surrendered during World War II

    D. to inform the reader about an event during World War II

2. Why did the U.S. drop atomic bombs on Japan?

    A. to end the fighting

    B. to engage Japan in battle

    C. to gain an ally

    D. to conquer territory

3. Which of the following best states the reason for the final paragraph?

    A. It provides the name of the bomb and the plane used to carry it.

    B. It describes how Japan was affected by the bomb.

    C. It explains why the bomb was used.

    D. It informs the reader about Japan's mission to abolish nuclear weapons.

4. According to the passage, which statement is true?

    A. The bomb spared the lives of Japanese civilians.

    B. Harry Truman opposed the use of the atomic bomb.

    C. Only one atomic bomb was dropped during World War II.

    D. A new word was created to describe the survivors of the attacks.

5. As used in the passage, the word *casualties* most nearly means

    A. negotiations.

    B. battles.

    C. deaths.

    D. struggles.

6. *Answer the following question using complete sentences:*

What does Truman's quote say about his willingness to negotiate peacefully with Japan?

DIRECTIONS: *Read the passage and answer the questions that follow it.*

George Washington Carver

GEORGE WASHINGTON CARVER was born in 1864, in Missouri, on Moses Carver's farm. As a small child, George was kidnapped, along with other members of his family, and sold by Confederates. Moses found only George, brought him home, and raised him as his own son. Moses never found the other members of George's family. At the age of twelve, George Carver moved to southwest Missouri to receive an education in a **segregated**, one-room schoolhouse. Carver became the first African-American student to attend Simpson College in Indianola, Iowa, at the age of thirty. Since the institution did not offer science classes, he transferred to Iowa Agricultural College (now Iowa State University) in 1891, and earned a Bachelor of Science degree in 1894, and a Master of Science degree in bacterial botany and agriculture in 1897.

Later in 1897, Carver became the director of the Tuskegee Normal and Industrial Institute for Negroes, which was founded by Booker T. Washington. While there, Carver developed a farming method based on the nitrogen cycle, called crop rotation, which revolutionized agricultural processes in the South. His method taught farmers to switch from **soil-depleting** crops, such as cotton, to soil-enriching crops, such as peanuts. To convince farmers to plant these profitable crops, he created recipes and developed uses for the plants. Known as "The Peanut Man," the agricultural chemist discovered more than 300 uses for peanuts and hundreds for soybeans, pecans, and sweet potatoes. This greatly affected the economy of the United States and helped revitalized Southern devastation resulting from the Civil War. During World War I, Carver used agricultural innovation to improve America's industry. After finding a way to replace textile dyes previously imported from Europe, he created 500 different shades and invented a process for producing paints and stains from soybeans. His invention in 1927 led to three separate patents. He also made improvements to, or created recipes for bleach, ink, plastic, talcum powder, and many more items used today. In regard to Carver's ideas, he would say, "God gave them to me. How could I sell them to someone else?" In 1940, he used his life's savings to create the Carver Research Foundation to support continued agricultural research at Tuskegee, where he spent the rest of his life researching and teaching. George Washington Carver died in 1943. ●

QUESTIONS

1. Which of the following best states the author's purpose?
   A. to show how African-Americans contributed to the economy during the Civil War
   B. to inform the reader about the many possible uses of peanuts
   C. to explain why George Washington Carver is important
   D. to describe how crop rotation benefits agriculture

2. What is the reason for the first paragraph?
   A. It describes Carver's life as a slave.
   B. It informs the reader about the practice of slave raids during the Civil War.
   C. It describes how Carver received an education during difficult times for African-Americans.
   D. It demonstrates Moses Carver's role in raising George Carver.

3. Which of the following would be the best title for this passage?
   A. African-American Agriculture
   B. The Peanut Man
   C. The Patent King
   D. Peanuts for Profit

4. According to the information provided, which statement is true?
   A. Carver worked at African-American institutions but never taught at one.
   B. Carver helped provide more profits for farmers.
   C. Carver's invention was patented during World War II.
   D. Carver's education was similar to that received by African-Americans today.

5. As used in the passage, the word *soil-depleting* most nearly means
   A. decreasing nutrients.
   B. increasing productivity.
   C. stabilizing volume.
   D. providing fertility.

6. *Answer the following question using complete sentences:*
   What does Carver's quotation say about his character?

DIRECTIONS: *Read the passage and answer the questions that follow it.*

Fast Food

Although fast food has existed since Ancient Roman cities featured bread and olive stands, modern fast food began with the hamburger. White Castle, which opened in 1921, is credited with pioneering the fast food industry with its five-cent hamburgers. Since White Castle's **inception**, numerous chains, such as Taco Bell, KFC, and Burger King, have joined the competition. McDonald's, currently the largest fast food chain in the world, opened in 1955. Wendy's, which opened in 1972, created the "drive-thru" window. Fast food is now a multibillion dollar industry that is saturating our culture and clogging our arteries.

To many Americans, fast food is a way of life, demonstrating our emphasis on speed and immediate results. Left with little time to prepare food for our families or ourselves, we look to fast food to come to our rescue. With various options for breakfast, lunch, and dinner, people are eating out or taking food home in record numbers. Cheeseburgers, tacos, chicken nuggets, and french-fries are flying from under heating lamps, out the drive thru window, and straight to our waistlines. Since fast food items are highly processed and prepared in bulk (then kept hot or reheated), quality and freshness comparable to a home-cooked meal are not factors for most restaurants. Because so many foodstuffs are high in fat, deep fried in oil, or high in sugar, Americans are gaining weight.

For example, in a meal consisting of a cheeseburger, medium fries, and reduced fat vanilla cone from McDonald's, the nutritional values are as follows: 840 total calories, 36 grams of fat, and 1020 milligrams of sodium. In attempts to illustrate potential health concerns, a documentary called *Super Size Me* was made in 2004, by Morgan Spurlock, who ate nothing but McDonald's for thirty days. Having gained significant weight and having become physically ill, he drew national attention to the harmful effects of a diet consisting entirely of fast food. On the other hand, some fast food companies, such as Subway, have promoted their foodstuffs, along with exercise, as part of a healthy weight loss program. With more criticism and pressure from **consumer** groups, chains have added healthier choices, such as yogurt and salads, to their menus. Just be sure to stay away from the fries! ●

QUESTIONS

1. Which of the following best states the author's purpose?
   A. to describe the history of the fast food industry
   B. to explain why Americans eat so much fast food
   C. to describe potential health risks of fast food consumption
   D. to explain why McDonald's is an international chain

2. Why does the author mention Morgan Spurlock?
   A. to highlight the problem with a diet consisting entirely of fast food
   B. to emphasize the benefits of exercise in conjunction with a healthy diet
   C. to convince fast food chains to serve healthy foods
   D. to support the notion that fast food is part of our society

3. Which of the following best states the author's personal view of the fast food industry?
   A. Consuming fast food puts all Americans at serious health risk.
   B. Fast food chains are the sole reason Americans are becoming obese.
   C. It is important to make healthful choices when consuming fast food.
   D. Americans eat fast food because they are too lazy to cook.

4. As used in the passage, the word *inception* most nearly means
   A. opening.
   B. creation.
   C. building.
   D. conception.

5. According to the passage, which statement is true?
   A. Fast food restaurants are a modern creation.
   B. It is impossible to lose weight by eating fast food.
   C. Burger King created the "drive-thru" window to compete with McDonalds.
   D. McDonald's is the most popular fast food chain in the world.

6. *Answer the following question using complete sentences:*
   Why is it important to make healthy food choices?

DIRECTIONS: *Read the passage and answer the questions that follow it.*

Mega-Tsunami

On July 9, 1958, the peacefulness and tranquility of a scenic Alaskan bay was abruptly broken by a sudden, massive wave known as a mega-tsunami. Lituya Bay, which is located on the northeastern shore of the Gulf of Alaska, has been the scene of at least four such giant waves during the past 200 years. The 1958 wave, however, is the best documented and most-studied of the four.

At approximately 10:15 P.M., on July 9, the area around the bay, which borders the Fairweather fault, experienced an 8.3 **magnitude** earthquake. This is equivalent to the 1906 San Francisco quake, which killed thousands and reduced the city to ruins.

On the evening of July 9, there were three boats in Lituya Bay. The crew of two of the boats survived, and their accounts reveal an amazing story of perhaps the largest tsunami witnessed in modern times. Howard Ulrich and William Swanson, each aboard his own craft, provided their first-hand accounts of the event. Both reported feeling the earthquake, which was followed by a massive rockslide on the side of the mountain at the head of the bay, which splashed water an amazing 1720 feet up the mountains. Both men reported what

they described as a "deafening crash." Next came a gigantic, 100-foot wave traveling towards the Gulf at speeds upward of ninety miles per hour. The wave lifted the boats and carried them over land, re-depositing them in the water. Ulrich's boat washed back into the bay. He and his son describe the **subsequent** splashing of waves back and forth in the bay, similar to water disrupted in a tub, littered with logs and trees. Swanson's boat rode the wave approximately eighty feet above the treetops and crashed into the Gulf. He and his wife were rescued several hours later. The occupants of the third boat, sadly, perished in the wave. The force of this massive tsunami gushed inland approximately 3600 feet, cleared more than four square miles, and washed away millions of trees.

Although the Lituya Bay tsunami was indeed a tremendous phenomenon of deadly force, it in no way rivals other, less powerful tsunamis that have caused massive human devastation around the world. Perhaps the fortune in this event was that the land around the bay was uninhabited; there were no nearby cities, towns, or villages. Had there been any, they most assuredly would have been completely obliterated. ●

QUESTIONS

1. **What triggered this mega-tsunami?**
   - **A.** a rockslide
   - **B.** an earthquake
   - **C.** a giant wave
   - **D.** an avalanche

2. **Why does the author mention that William Swanson's boat rode the wave eighty feet above the treetops?**
   - **A.** to prove that some trees remained standing
   - **B.** to compare Swanson's experience to Ulrich's experience
   - **C.** to explain Swanson's fear
   - **D.** to illustrate the size of the wave

3. **Why does the author mention the San Francisco earthquake of 1906?**
   - **A.** to explain why it was fortunate that there were no cities near Lituya Bay
   - **B.** to show how much destruction earthquakes can cause
   - **C.** to provide an example of the Lituya earthquake's magnitude
   - **D.** to demonstrate how earthquakes can cause tsunamis

4. **Based on the passage, which of the following is true?**
   - **A.** The Lituya Bay tsunami of 1958 had no significant impact on the surrounding area.
   - **B.** The Lituya Bay tsunami of 1958 was the only giant wave to have hit Lituya Bay.
   - **C.** The Lituya Bay tsunami of 1958 was the most destructive wave in recent history.
   - **D.** The Lituya Bay tsunami of 1958 is probably the largest wave witnessed in recent history.

5. **As used in the passage, the word *subsequent* most nearly means**
   - **A.** resultant.
   - **B.** continuous.
   - **C.** expanding.
   - **D.** destructive.

6. **Which of the following most accurately states the result of a tsunami this size hitting America's eastern shore?**
   - **A.** There would be massive devastation.
   - **B.** A few buildings would be destroyed.
   - **C.** Trees would be uprooted.
   - **D.** People would experience large waves.

DIRECTIONS: *Read the passage and answer the questions that follow it.*

Laughter

THE MEDICAL COMMUNITY has proven that laughter indeed carries a healing property. The act of laughing stimulates circulation, boosts the immune system, and releases the tension that builds up and becomes what we call stress. Numerous doctors have attempted to include humor in their treatment of patients, but the absolutely best application would also involve genuine care and **compassion**, which most medical professionals attempt to achieve and communicate. The reality is, however, that medicine has become an industry, driven by profits. This is not to assert that doctors are motivated by profits, but it does imply that insurance companies are. It is this need for profit that indirectly sets quotas for how many patients a doctor must see in a day, thereby limiting the amount of time a patient can spend in the examination room. Because of this time limit, most patients and doctors cannot truly get to know each other and develop a friendly, compassionate relationship.

One man, however, has made it his mission to change the system. Dr. Patch Adams, M.D., has spent nearly forty years endeavoring to institute social change that will return the care to healthcare. His Gesundheit! Institute includes a community clinic and plans for a hospital, which do not charge patients and refuse third party payments. Staff and patients live there together while care is being administered. Essentially, the employees and the patients become friends and family, all working together to reach the ultimate goal: healing. He believes in fostering friendship and joy, those intangibles that truly establish a healthy person. The x-rays, MRI's, and blood tests that prove a person is healthy completely ignore the emotional health of the patient. As people, we need to trust and belong, and Patch Adams has been working diligently with a team of believers to bring about a joyous, inclusive, supportive, and friendly health care system that works. He has taken his message of compassionate care, involved community, and laughter as medicine around the world. Despite the popularity brought to him by the 1988 movie bearing his **namesake**, Patch Adams is very down-to-earth, hoping that people will embark on just one seemingly simple, yet vastly important, mission from his quest to promote a healthy, happy, and compassionate communal society. His humble request? "Please give your life to peace, justice and care." **❍**

QUESTIONS

1. **Which of the following would be the best title for this passage?**
   A. Healthcare Profits
   B. Best Friends
   C. Laughter Is the Best Medicine
   D. X-Rays, MRI's, and Blood Tests

2. **According to the passage, which member of the medical community is motivated by profits?**
   A. bill collectors
   B. insurance companies
   C. doctors and hospitals
   D. patients

3. **What is Patch Adams' message to the world?**
   A. Find a doctor who believes in laughter.
   B. Support the medical community.
   C. Devote all of your time to others.
   D. Care about others.

4. **Which of the following best summarizes Dr. Adams' ideal medical community?**
   A. communal, compassionate, friendly
   B. unsmiling, communal, devoted
   C. compassionate, bureaucratic, friendly
   D. profitable, free, communal

5. **Which of the following is not a result of laughter?**
   A. increased circulation
   B. decreased stress
   C. slowed healing
   D. bolstered immune system

6. **As used in the passage, the word *compassion* would most likely lead to**
   A. disorientation.
   B. friendship.
   C. healing.
   D. anger.